C000180189

100 year history of the Sick Berth Branch

Gregory Clark

London   HER MAJESTY'S STATIONERY OFFICE

ISBN 0 11 290427 0

Contents

Foreword

The Royal Naval Sick Berth Branch was introduced by Order in Council in 1884 and this book has been produced to celebrate the centenary of its formation. As will be seen from Commander Clark's fascinating and detailed account, the branch had its origins long before this time and has continued to adapt its rôle to meet the needs of the Royal Naval of today

The book is divided into three parts. The first chapter traces the history of the Royal Naval Medical Service and presents an interesting potted history of its development. The next three chapters are a specific summary of the progress of the Medical Assistant which includes the most recent changes in training and branch structure and will be of particular interest to retired members of the branch. The final three chapters include an informative chapter on past and present Hospital Ships and Training Hospitals and a final one on Honours, and Awards as well as reminiscences from retired branch members.

Commander Clark is a retired Instructor Commander, Royal Navy, who served with the RN Medical Service as the 'Schoolie' at RN Hospital, Haslar from 1950–52. During this time he introduced a hospital magazine called *NAVOSP*. Since retiring from the Royal Navy he has worked for the Naval Museum in the Portsmouth Naval Base where he has become an expert on *'Britain's Naval Heritage'* – the title of one of his previous books. In *'Doc'* he has produced an excellent factual account of the history of the Sick Berth Branch together with a nostalgic section of personal reminiscences.

I commend the book to both Service and non-service readers alike; there will be few readers who fail to find it of interest ·

R. J. W. LAMBERT
Surgeon Vice Admiral
Medical Director General (Naval)   June 1984
Ministry of Defence
London.

Acknowledgements

When invited to write the history of the Royal Naval Sick Berth Branch, I accepted readily for two reasons. Firstly because of a general interest in most aspects of naval history and secondly because of my personal association with members of its branch many of whom I taught as a young officer when on the staff of the Royal Naval Hospital, Haslar.

That appointment gave me first hand experience of the branch and prompted me to enquire into its origins, a task which I have now researched in more detail. In this I have received considerable assistance from ex-branch members, their relatives and descendants who collectively have supplied me with a wealth of material which spans the last hundred years. Where relevant to the text, references to these contributions have been made whilst a separate chapter has been reserved for a cross section of some of their reminiscences. I have already corresponded with all who have so kindly contributed and once again, I offer all concerned my sincere thanks.

On the more official side I am also indebted to the following personalities each of whom in their various ways have made my task easier in the paths of research:

Captain R. H. Parsons MA, Royal Navy (Rtd)
>Director, Royal Naval Museum Portsmouth

Surgeon Captain R. W. F. Paul MB ChB MSc Royal Navy
>Director Naval Medical Staff School, RN Hospital, Haslar

Commander M. G. Harper MA, MSc, Royal Navy
>Head of the Medical Services Branch, Ministry of Defence

C. T. Parsons Esq
>Curator and Librarian, RN Hospital, Haslar

Jack Fitch Esq.
>Secretary to the RN Sick Berth Staff and Retired Members Association

(at the time of its dissolution).

Except where stated otherwise, the photographs and illustrations in this booklet have been supplied by the courtesy of E. L. Over Esq, Clinical Photographer, RN Hospital, Haslar.

CHAPTER ONE

Early Naval Medical Care

The first mention of the obligation to care for sick seaman appears in the Laws of Oleron upon which the present Naval Discipline Act is based. Sometimes known as the judgements of Oleron and dating from circa 1194, they are themselves based on the code of conduct founded in the Republic of Rhodes and adopted by the Romans and other maritime powers of the Mediterranean. They took their name from a small island off the coast of France which in earlier times was a great rendez-vous for merchant ships especially those engaged in the wine trade.

Amongst the many laws, some of which were undoubtedly harsh by today's standards, was the following compassionate reference. If a mariner falls sick and becomes incapable of working, the Master was to put him ashore and seek a lodging for him, provide him moreover with a candle of tallow and one of the ship's boys to tend him, or failing that, a hired women. King Richard Coeur de Lion introduced these laws into England having first met them during the Crusades where the forces included a strong contingent from Oleron and thus from his day it became customary for a sick seamen whose illnesses or disabilities were due to their service, to expect treatment and care at the expense of the ship's owner or captain. Before long sea voyages were made, there was no demand for ship's surgeons and during medieval times this lack of specific naval medical provision was partly due to the outcome of the navy's primary role as a transport service and the fact that all sea fights took place within easy reach of our coasts. To have a law is one thing but to enforce it is another and the poor unfortunate disabled mariner of medieval days often found himself homeless. There existed hospitals of a kind – they were known as Houses of Pity – and were run by monks of various religious orders and really intended as travellers resting places whilst making pilgrimages to cathedrals, churches and shrines. Except for the two London Hospitals of St Bartholmew's and St Thomas's, sick and invalided seamen sufficiently fortunate to find a caring body would find themselves in the institutions of a religious order of monks.

Such nursing was excellent for the times but it must be remembered that the whole attitude to nursing and medicine was influenced by the Church. Hippocrates, that renowned Greek physician, affectionately known as the Father of Medicine, taught that knowledge was the result of observation. The Church had its own ideas and in a Papal Bull or edict of 1308, it decreed that all students of medicine, and there were many among the clergy, were obliged to study only prescribed works and the Scriptures, the translations of which from the Arabic, Greek and Latin, were often imperfect. As early causes of disease were considered to be the result of an imbalance of what were known as the four humours – heat, cold, moistness, and dryness thus causing 'bad' blood, the removal of some of it was thought to be the panacea for almost all ills save those of the very common variety.

When, however, it came to the operation of 'bloodletting' medieval surgery was crude. As the old name 'chirurgeon' implies, he was one who worked with his hands but unfortunately those who were recognised as qualified medical men were members of religious fraternities who were strictly forbidden (by a Papal decree of 1215) to bloodlet, not even to lance a boil. Most of these men who supervised Houses of Pity were well educated in one or more of the three recognised faculties, Divinity, Law and Medicine. Unfortunately, Medicine and Surgery were not then branches of one profession nor were they to become so for hundreds of years ahead. The problem of who was to be the 'bloodletter' was quickly solved by the barber. Familiar as he was with the use of the razor, he only required a few lectures from a learned father on the finer points of bloodletting to herald his appearance in the community as the 'Barber-surgeon'. By 1424 a charter was given to the new guild of 'Barber-Surgeons'.

On occasions, medical men had been known to work with the army and navy but as there was no definite distinction between army and navy surgeons, it is difficult to give an exact date for the appointment of a sea-surgeon. It is known that when so appointed or attached to a force it was for the personal attention to the King, as at Agincourt in 1415, or to the Ship's Captain.

As ships became larger and voyages longer, they carried more men and were away from their home ports sometimes for years at a stretch. The first warship to have carried broadside guns was the 'Mary Rose' but in the minds of most naval historians the first battleship of note was Henry VIII's 'Henry Grace a Dieu' known as the *Great Harry*. Commissioned in 1514, she carried as many sailors as soldiers. This was the beginning of a new era, one of longer voyages and the transporting of great numbers of men and one requiring the use of sea-surgeons. Towards the end of Henry's reign, he dissolved the monasteries and simultaneously, the Houses of Pity, the sanctuaries where so many invalided and wounded seamen had received rest and treatment.

In 1544 a French Fleet, which was to support any invasion of this country, was defeated by an epidemic caused by food-poisoning. It spread quickly to the English Fleet and later in 1577 when Calais was lost, the same thing occurred and there was no idea of how to cope with the disease. Probably the culminating disaster was in 1588, after the defeat by the Queen's seamen of the Spanish Armada. Food poisoning decimated the English Fleet and seamen in their hundreds perished by the wayside in the streets of British seaports. Food poisoning had struck yet again. This disease as well as others that were recognised by experienced sea-captains and one or two physicians who had been attached to the Fleet, diseases of typhus, smallpox and the ever present scurvy proved to all that the problem of their cure was not a surgical matter but rather a medical internal affair.

Those who did survive petitioned Queen Elizabeth for relief. The outcome was the establishment in 1588 of the 'Chatham Chest' Fund, the income for which was obtained by the monthly levy from the wages of every officer and rating of 6 old pence per head for the payment to those seamen who were maimed or wounded as a result of the injuries sustained during the war – the amount of each pension being dependent upon the extent of their injuries. These pensions varied from £12 annually (for the loss of 2 eyes) to £4 annually (for the loss of 1 eye, and fracture of the skull). The actual chest was kept in the South porch of Chatham Parish Church until 1893 when it was moved to Greenwich, and its funds invested in Government securities. The 6 old pence levy was stopped in 1829 and the remaining balance was paid to the Treasurer of the Navy for expenditure on naval pensions.

In the reign of Elizabeth I, famous mariners such as Drake and his cousin Hawkins in their sea voyages had discovered that Portugese seamen drank the juices of 'sower oranges and lemmons' as a scurvy preventative, a practice which they encouraged their own crews to follow. Little did they realise that had this custom become universal it would have eliminated the disease. Both seamen were very enterprising and had great faith in the ship's surgeon who they insisted on including in their complement. Drake in particular had health ideas of his own and had a great fetish concerning minimising the number of clothes worn by his crew, thinking that the greater number carried was the possible source of disease. He wrote 'scurvie might be kept at bay by shifts and men should not bring to sea more cloathes than they have on their backs'.

It does appear that many British Tudor warships carried one of the new breed of barber-surgeons and it is apparent from the medical artefacts recovered from the Mary Rose that their medical knowledge was of a wider scope than once thought. Such artefacts now displayed in the Mary Rose Museum in the Portsmouth Naval Base include a surgeon's medical chest from which wooden and ceramic medicine jars were removed, some of them bearing traces of their contents. Two, when examined, revealed Frankincense, which was used in ointment form as a cure for ulcers, and peppercorns, the latter being thought to have been taken by patients suffering from fevers.

Also displayed is a barber surgeon's coif – a close fitting head covering cap made of white lawn – which was a symbol of importance and which appears in many old oil paintings depicting Tudor Barber surgeons.

Until the period of the Commonwealth the official attitude to the care of the sick and wounded remained unaltered, if a man was disabled he was really left to fend for himself. The Commonwealth Council tapping new sources of wealth from the estates of the defeated Cavaliers tried to create a 'New Model Navy' and established the 'Commissioners for the Sick and Hurt' to cater for disabled seamen, even issuing gratuities and sometimes pensions for seamen no longer able to serve. Many London hospitals were ordered to provide beds for seamen and similar orders were given to smaller hospitals in the naval seaports. Such humanitarian attitudes did not last and once again the disabled seaman was left to his own devices. Even the establishment of the Chatham Chest fund was unsatisfactory. Applicants were obliged to apply personally at Chatham and few could afford the journey, the fund thus increased and sums of money were embezzled. There followed several enquiries and it was agreed that travelling expenses should be paid to applicants for sick relief and that some of the Fund should be used to build Naval hospitals for seamen. Gradually the abuses ceased and small pensions were awarded to the disabled, small indeed by modern standards but it must be remembered that in the early part of the 17th Century the annual wages of a barber-surgeon was no more than £50. With his salary agreed on first appointment he was also paid a sum of money, usually in the order of £10, as an allowance for the purchase of his surgeon's chest which contained essential surgical instruments and a selection of drugs for use at sea.

Apart from the assistance given by the Chatham Fund, sick seamen in common with the man in the street had to rely on the arrangements made with London and seaport hospitals for care and those unable to so benefit, had to find assistance in either the few almshouses that existed, or seek accommodation in taverns or private homes. The Hospitals, particularly those in London, did not like the reservation of special beds for seamen despite the promises of the Sick and Hurt Board that all expenses incurred in their care, wherever accommodated would be refunded. John Evelyn who wrote such valuable accounts of this period was given the responsibility for the sick and wounded of the Dutch Wars, also for the Dutch prisoners but found the tasks unenviable because Government funds were entirely inadequate. Such was the crux of the matter, the Government accepted the responsibility of caring for their sick mariners but had no money to support their promises. All the while the Commissioners for the Sick and Hurt Board continually pressed the authorities to do something and inevitably with no funds available, little or nothing happened and much was left to Charity. In this connection probably the first great naval nurse came into the public eye. She was an Elizabeth Alkin, although she was better known as 'Parliamentary

Joan', and she provided at her own expense, valuable services to sick and wounded seamen during the Dutch Wars. She organised a team of nurses in Harwich to care for wounded sailors and those who could be accomodated in the London Hospitals, she took there herself, expending her own funds in providing transport for four wagons of wounded men. The precedent in the establishment of the Sick and Hurt Board was a welcome change though initially their suggested reforms achieved little. At least the acknowledgement by the Government that it had accepted the principle of responsibility for the care of sick seamen was an achievement even though nothing practical resulted.

Meanwhile there had been improvements in the medical field though mainly in administration. In 1617 the Society of Apothecaries received a Charter. Apart from the dispensing of medicines, an Apothecary kept stocks of surgical instruments and medical chests which were sold to barber surgeons when appointed to warships. To ensure that the medicines and surgical instruments were up to required standards. Henry VIII gave the elite body of doctors, the College of Physicians, the right of inspection of an Apothecary's stores. When the same right was given to the Company of Barber Surgeons it only increased the feeling of rivalry between the physician and surgeon, the former being considered as a scholar and a gentleman, whilst the surgeon was thought of as a journeyman and craftsman.

One such member of the latter fraternity was John Woodall who was appointed surgeon to the East India Company in 1612. He provided the surgeons aboard the Company's Fleet with their medical chests and later he became Surgeon to St Bartholmew's Hospital.

Though he himself never served at sea, his book 'Surgeons Mate' published in 1617, gives the reader a fair idea of conditions then prevailing. As the name implies a surgeon's mate was an assistant to the surgeon and could become a surgeon through experience. Woodhall strongly upheld the need for ship's surgeons to be able to give internal medicines to patients and he emphasised the value of orange and lemon juices for their curative effects on the disease of scurvy, but like earlier opinions on the same lines, these views were treated with great scepticism by other medical men. In his book are instructions to his 'barber's boy' on how to use a syringe thus indicating that a surgeon (and his mate) had some assistance with their work. It is interesting to note that about the same time as the publication, the expression 'loblolly' boy is first noted. The Oxford Dictionary lists the following definition Loblolly – first used in 1597 and derived from 'Lob' to bubble or boil especially porridge and 'lolly' – broth boiled in a pot.

In the Royal Navy, and in other navies which copied, the expression 'loblolly' boy was first associated with anyone who helped the surgeon as an odd job man. Usually, the work was undertaken by a seaman, young or old who, not being efficient as such, was directed by his

Captain to be a 'waister' that is his work should be confined to the area of the ship's waist and not be permitted to work aloft. It was indeed a relegation to what was considered a lower standard of work. Though technically a 'waister' the loblolly boy was employed in battle in the ship's cockpit, a compartment way below the main decks, access to which was achieved by descending a series of hatchway ladders. It was to this area that the wounded were brought for surgery. When the loblolly boy was not making up medicines or winding bandages he could be seen spoonfeeding invalids with broth or burgoo – a kind of maritime porridge. From this latter duty he soon earned his soubriquet and its naval meaning was assimilated into the English vocabulary.

More power was given to the Company of Barber Surgeons when they were requested to administer all arrangements for the entry of sea surgeons to the Royal Navy. Judging however from the types of surgeons they did admit, their selection methods were very suspect. On some occasions they were obliged to enforce their entries by use of the Acts of Impressment when because of the increase in the numbers of warships, more surgeons were needed. Certainly the practice of having surgeons aboard warships of any reasonable size increased even also their use in hospital ships. From available records it does appear that the first vessel to warrant such a title was the *Goodwill* which joined the Mediterranean Fleet in 1620. She was either a converted fifth rate warship, ie one that carried around 32 cannon, or a converted merchantman. To make the ship more hygienic, gratings were cut in the wooden side plankings so as to increase ventilation. The *Goodwill* is known to have carried one surgeon and a surgeon's mate and three 'attendants' the inference being that these were really loblolly boys. Together with a crew of seamen and some soldiers for other duties, they made up the complement of the ship. As soon as wars ceased however, all these arrangements lapsed for there was no continuous naval service and ship's complements were dismissed and the sick were, in so many cases, left to their own devices. Samuel Pepys, that renowned diarist and the First Secretary to the Admiralty in the mid 17th century on noting seamen in London after the Second Dutch wars wrote 'the lamentable cries came from a crowd of seamen who lie starving in the streets for lack of money which does trouble me to the heart; more I saw at noon when a whole hundred of them followed, some cursing, some swearing and some crying to us for help'. With such a graphic picture of sailors who had at least managed to make their way to London, one can image the more dreadful scenes Pepys might have witnessed had he seen the sick and disabled mariners in the almshouses and byways of the naval seaports.

Relief was promised by the foundation of the Royal Hospital at Greenwich in 1694 by William and Mary for the 'relief and support of seamen who by reason of age, wounds and other disabilities shall be incapable of further service at sea'.

The promised relief in fact did not arrive until the end of the century when the first 42 patients were admitted; the fact that it did prove necessary was shown by the end of that century when its invalids and pensioners numbered almost 3000.

Earlier in the year of its foundation a William Cockburn MD joined the Fleet as a surgeon. He was to prove a most conscientious doctor and one of particular note. In his writings he mentioned the inadequacy of the normal prescribed diet for the sick sailor – a barley water type of gruel – which made patients costive. He complained that there was no specific compartment on board a man of war where the sick could be treated and stated that his up patients had to be summoned for daily treatment by the sounding of an alarm call. This call was made by his 'loblolly' boy striking a mortar with a pestle whilst he walked around the ship. It was a signal for the sick to repair to the ship's mainmast where in good weather, treatment was given; if the weather was unfavourable, patients would congregate outside the surgeon's cabin for attention. As for those unable or too sick to walk, they were seen by the surgeon in their messes where their messmates acted as nurses.

During the final Dutch War and in the first of the many wars which began against France in 1689, increasing use was made of Hospital Ships. Like the 'Goodwill' of earlier vintage, these vessels were either converted men of war or hired merchant ships. They carried a quota of surgeons and nurses, none of the latter with any previous training for attending the sick. Mainly pressed men were used and in some ships women acted as nurses. Records show that the use of Hospital ships was very popular amongst the surgeons but mixed opinions were expressed as to which sex made the better nurse.

Usually the women were either seamen's widows or wives who worked as nurses when ships were berthed in Home Ports, but much depended upon the whims of the warship's Commanding Officer. Some occasionally brought their own wives to sea and allowed their crews the same privilege; others were very much against the practice. Men frequently smuggled females on board by the most devious ways and these ladies often remained and were present during many of the sea battles against the French when they served as nurses to the wounded. Expressions such as 'Show a leg' and 'Son of a gun' thus originated, the first from the custom of allowing women an extra half-hour in their hammocks when the hands were called for morning duties. The sudden projection from a hammock of a shapely leg in reply to the boatswain's call satisfied him that the occupant was truly a female and he continued his call elsewhere. As for 'Son of a Gun' this name was given to a child born in a Man of War. Any woman who found herself in labour was taken below to the main gun deck, where, alongside one of the cannon a canvas screen was erected and there her child was born. Sometimes in cases of a difficult labour it is recorded in some ships' logs that the surgeon requested the

Captain that the ship might fire a broadside as the thunder of the guns and effects of recoil often precipitated the birth. At the Battle of the Glorious First of June in 1794, a Mrs McKenzie serving in HMS *Tremendous* found herself in labour at the height of the action against the French. Taken below, she gave birth to a son whom she christened Daniel Tremendous McKenzie. Years later, when Daniel was in his fifties, he received the Naval General Service Medal with the added clasp 'First of June 1794' and around the rim of this medal inscribed before his name, was rating or 'quality' as 'Baby'.

Eventually the recommendations of the Sick and Hurt Board were partly met by the opening of Haslar Hospital in 1754. As with hospital ships the nurses were female and were drawn from similar sources and were all untrained. It was an improvement however as formerly, sick and wounded seamen in the Portsmouth area were billeted ashore in taverns and hovels. Records show that in one year alone there were approximately 8000 accommodated in this manner, over 900 of whom died and a further 1000 absconded. In those days of course the press gangs operated and men from all walks of life were dragged away from their families and normal work for service with the Royal Navy, incidentally the title the service had been given by Charles II. It is understandable that many absconded when the opportunity arose and left Haslar Hospital in this manner. There were indeed more irregularities both by patients and nursing staff. In 1755, 25 men escaped from the hospital through a sewer and patients within the hospital openly bribed the nurses to bring in spirits; on one occasion an attempt was made to bring in 50 barrels of brandy from a ship anchored close to the hospital walls. Frequently gin and rum made their entry to the wards via pigs' bladders carried in by the nursing staff. Surgical treatment, mainly amputations remained crude. The unfortunate patient was lashed down to ring bolts on a wooden table, made as insensible as possible with rum, the limb amputated and the stump cauterised by immersion in boiling pitch. As for the condition of the wards within, a report made in 1789 stated 'the inside sewers are offensive, there are no cisterns in the wards and the pipes which supply drinking water adjoin the sewers'.

Conditions aboard a man of war were even worse and for a word picture Tobias Smollet, a one time surgeon's mate, must be thanked. He obtained some medical qualification in Glasgow in 1739 and travelled south to seek employment. Surgeons at that time were warrant officers and Smollet was granted a warrant for Royal Naval Service in 1740 and he served for four years. Leaving for private practice, he tried his hand at writing and his first novel 'Roderick Random' the story of a surgeon's mate, was so successful that he gave up medicine. The novel does throw considerable light on medical facilities in a man of war. After describing how Roderick entered the Service he described his accommodation adjoining the ship's cockpit — 'the place allotted for habitation of the surgeon's mate and when I had seen my berth, I was filled with astonishment and horror. I had descended by divers ladders to a space as dark as a dungeon, which I understood was immersed several feet under water, being immediately above the hold. I had no sooner approached the dismal gulf, than my nose was saluted with an intolerable stench of putrefied cheese and rancid butter that issued from an apartment at the foot of the ladder, resembling a chandler's shop, where, by the faint glimmering of a candle, I could perceive a man with a pale meagre countenance, sitting behind a kind of desk, having spectacles on his nose and a pen in his hand. This I learned was the ship's steward who sat there to distribute provisions to the several messes. Taking a light in his hand he conducted me to the place of his residence, which was a square about six feet surrounded by the medicine chest, that of the first mate, his own chest, and a board by way of a table fastened to the after powder room; it was enclosed with a canvas screen nailed to the beams of the ship, to screen us from the cold. In this gloomy space, he entertained me with some salt pork and calling for a boy, sent for a can of beer, of which he made excellent flip to crown the banquet'. Then Roderick was shown the sick berth in some other part of the ship and he describes it thus, 'I saw about 50 miserable distempered wretches so huddled one upon the other that not more than 14 inches space was allotted for each with his bed and bedding, and all deprived of the light of day as well as fresh air; breathing nothing but a vile atmosphere of the morbid steams exhaling from their own excrements and diseased bodies, devoured with vermin hatched in filth that surrounds them and destitute of every convenience necessary for people in that helpless condition. To this place the sick were summoned to have their sores dressed by a 'loblolly' boy who banged on a pestle and mortar'.

All was not gloom, there were glimpses of blue on the medical and nursing horizons. Some doctors, destined to leave their mark, were joining as sea surgeons. James Lind, an Edinburgh graduate, a great advocate in the curative effects of lemon juice in the cure of scurvy, became a naval surgeon in the middle of the 18th century. He wrote a 'Treatise on Scurvy' in 1754 though many years were to pass before his advice was put into practice. In 1752 another classic was published entitled 'Observations on Diseases of the Army' by Sir John Pringle, who had been a Professor of Moral Philosophy before his military career. During the War of the Austrian Succession, at the battle of Dettigen in 1741, yet one more of the periodic outbreaks in the century of wars against France, he suggested that military hospitals on both sides should be sanctuaries, a suggestion which led, eventually, to the establishment of the Red Cross, although the First Geneva Convention was not formed until 1863 at the instigation of a Swiss Banker, Jean Henri Dunant. A slackening in the social distinction between the physician and surgeon was eased by an Act of 1749 which permitted surgeons who had practised in the Army or Navy for three years to enter private practice without further examination and additionally, Apothecaries were given the right to dispense and prescribe medicines for patients. Differences still persisted however, particularly in naval hospitals ashore which by the end of the 18th century included one at Plymouth. The physician, having inherited from generations of his predecessors, an air of superiority over the surgeon was loath to alter his feelings and in this, he was not encouraged by conservative Admiralty views, their Lordships even allowing physicians to supervise the work of surgeons. Such views, translated locally went to further extremes, surgeons being obliged to write their notes in blue ink whilst the superior physicians used red and when the respective patients of the physicians and surgeons attended the hospital churches, they were obliged to occupy pews on opposite sides of the centre aisle rather like the separation of the brides and bridegrooms' guests at a wedding but unlike the outcome of a wedding, there was no marriage between the two medical factions. This silly situation persisted into the next century but when the Admiralty removed the title physician from the Navy List in 1840 leaving the only medical one of surgeon, the disparity gradually waned.

Another celebrated doctor who joined the navy as a physician, and like Mrs McKenzie of earlier mention, also served at the Battle of the Glorious First of June in 1794, was Thomas Trotter MD. A graduate of Edinburgh he became Physician to the Channel Fleet and later served at the Royal Naval Hospital, Haslar. He became widely respected for his many reforms, one of which was the removal of pigsties from their accustomed places in a warship. Because of the epidemics of food-poisoning attributed to the eating of contaminated meat and poultry, fresh food was carried in men of war in the form of live animals and fowls which were quartered in the manger, a compartment in the bows of the vessel. Trotter thought this was unhygienic and recommended their removal; he was also very concerned at the considerable drunkenness amongst sailors despite reductions in their issue of rum. He remarked that there were far too many public houses available in the naval ports and these enticed the sailors, with their pockets of prize money, to lighten their loads with detrimental effects. Illustrating this view, he stated that in the Plymouth dock area alone there were 120 inns, many of which were run and frequented by people of ill repute and he recommended that they should be kept in good order by patrolling constables. On the purely medical side he prescribed the introduction of lime juices as a scurvy preventative and of hot cocoa for seamen working in cold waters, above all he strongly supported the view so frequently suggested by naval surgeons that a separate compartment should be reserved in all men of war for the treatment and nursing of the sick.

CHAPTER TWO

Official recognition of the Sick Berth Branch

The fact that the views of medical men were beginning to take effect was shown by the elevation of naval surgeons to commissioned rank in 1805 but even before that date one of Dr Trotter's suggestions had already been acted upon by Admiral the Earl St Vincent who in 1798 was Commander-in-Chief of the Mediterranean Fleet. He was very keen to institute Sick Berth compartments in each ship under his command and gave orders accordingly, advising the layout of the new areas. These were to encompass the space in the ship's bows formerly containing the 'manger' and through which the chimney from the galley on the deck below passed, thus giving the new compartment or sick berth a kind of 'central heating'. At the turn of the century, Earl St Vincent had become First Lord of the Admiralty and in August 1801, this same order was given to the rest of the Royal Navy. In all First and Second Rates, the Sick Berth was placed in the area of the ship's bows but in smaller warships it was placed abreast the main hatchway. When the bows of warships became rounded, the name Sick Berth was altered to Sick Bay – the earliest use of the name, now so general throughout the Royal Navy appears to have been in 1813 on the *Namur*, the first purpose built warship with a round bow. The framing of the Bay was done by the use of canvas screens stretched on wooden battens. The Earl even named one first rate, the *Ville de Paris* as a model for all First rates to copy as he was so pleased with the Sick Bay therein. Attitudes were certainly improving even the loblolly boy was gaining in respect. Only a few years before the end of the century, one naval officer wrote of his boy as, 'a fellow of some small knowledge of reading and writing, who, by overhearing the daily clinical lectures of the doctor, contrives to pick up a smattering of medical terms, which he loses no opportunity of palming off upon his messmates below as sublime wisdom sucked in at Alma Mater'. After more experience however the same officer, a Captain Basil Hall RN in his book of reminiscences 'Voyages and Travels' published in 1860 in referring to the same loblolly boy, writes of 'his high intelligence and integrity – in as much as he has gained the admiration and respect of all manner of seamen aboard'.

The new title soon spread throughout the Fleet, sometimes prefixed by the Captain's name eg, Nelson's loblolly boy. Records show that at one time, Nelson had a certain Jack Rider so employed and his duties were recorded thus 'to do anything and everything required by the surgeon – from sweeping and washing the deck to saying 'Amen' to the Chaplain's prayers, from cleaning the guns to helping the surgeon to make pills, plasters and to mix medicines.' What is not stated, but no doubt taken for granted, are the commitments the boy had to the sick, feeding them and collecting the extra-tit bits of appetising foodstuffs given to the Sick Mess from the Captain's and Wardroom's tables. Another nickname acquired was 'poultice walloper' – the origin being obvious, but no matter the soubriquet, the very presence of a loblolly boy in the ship and his accessibility to all, made him an invaluable addition to a ship's complement.

When hostilities occurred between Britain and America in 1807, there were many ship-to-ship actions off the American coasts between the respective warships, mainly the frigate class – second in importance to ships of the line, fast, usually three masted and carrying up to 50 cannon. One such conflict was the action between the USS *Chesapeake* and HMS *Shannon* just off the Boston coast. The smaller British warship opened fire at 50 yards range and a heavy engagement followed resulting in the two vessels becoming intermeshed alongside one another with riggings entwined. Using the lofty entanglements as a bridge, the British boarded the American and she surrendered. A William Brown was the *Chesapeake's* loblolly boy but he also doubled as a trumpeter. Unfortunately, on that fateful day, 1 Jun 1813, he was somewhat dilatory in sounding the bugle call to 'Repel boarders' and his name is remembered in American naval history for this reason. Later, for his lack of action, he was courtmartialled. The incident just illustrates that loblolly boys, although perhaps not proficient seamen, could show versatility in other spheres.

In 1827, the Melville hospital at Chatham opened its doors under the courtesy title of 'Royal Naval Hospital, Chatham' though the purpose built RN Hospital, Chatham was not completed until 1905. With the expansion of British Trade and the need to establish overseas stations, there were four places in 1833 which boasted the imposing name 'hospital' – Malta, Jamaica, Bermuda and Simonstown, as well as around forty 'Sick Quarters' in the British Isles. More doctors and nurses were required but none had any security of tenure, for great use was made of the 'hire and fire' principle in the continued use of the Press Gangs. In the purely medical field treatments had vastly improved though 'blood letting' as nature's cure for any complaint was still practised. The famous Dr William Beatty, Nelson's Surgeon, knighted and who earned the nations' gratitude for the part he played at Trafalgar, retired shortly after the battle and set up a practice in London which soon became popular. A certain Captain Dillon became his patient in 1821 suffering from an earlier wound which had not healed effectively. The illustrious doctor diagnosed the cause as an excess of blood and decided that treatment should consist of 'repeated bleedings from the jugular vein'. After several bleedings and starvation diet, Captain Dillon was reduced to the lowest degree of debility. Learning of the repute of a doctor in Dunkirk, Dillon crossed the Channel for new advice and the treatment recommended was the very reverse of Beatty's. He quickly recovered with a treatment of a full diet, plenty of wine, sea bathing and exercise. It appeared that Captain Dillon had been suffering from anaemia. Later he met Dr Beatty and lost no time in informing him of his faulty diagnosis. This example illustrates that despite the advances in medical knowledge throughout the 18th century and the many fine doctors who did appear, like the Royal Navy the profession was still somewhat conservative in its ideas.

Naval Medical Officers did not have charge of the main home hospitals, this privilege being given to executive naval officers and although surgeons had achieved the same ranking as naval lieutenants, in seniority they ranked 'after' them. Eventually these social distinctions were removed and the heads of the large home hospitals were given to surgeons, and as 'heads of departments' they were promoted to the rank of Commander. The hospital staff were of course women, some of very doubt ful morals with very 'easy' virtues. A small number of men reinforced them as casual labourers, originally employed to scrub floors, but they sometimes even nursed the sick. As already outlined, at sea, apart from some of the hospital ships, the nurses were loblolly boys, some exceedingly versatile but like their women shore counterparts, they were completely lacking in any form of nursing training. So the situation remained until 1833 when a directive was issued to the Commanding Officers in the Fleet to organise a 'Sick Berth Attendant' category of naval rating in each ship. From that date the new title appears in the wages tables of the Navy together with their varied rates of pay viz:

Assistant Sick Berth Attendant	1s4d daily (6½p)
Sick Berth Attendant	1s9d daily (9p)
Sick Berth Steward	2s5d daily (12p)

Small increments were given to the two higher rates for precise years of completed service. Known as 'badge' pay, one badge was awarded for 5 years, two badges for 10 and the maximum of three badges for 15. These periods have been changed over the years but badges are still worn on the left arm of ratings' uniform. When they were first introduced sailors wore the badges on a type of rig that most sailors had adopted, a blouse or frock as it was known which was worn over ankle length trousers.

Promotion from one rate to another was haphazard and depended upon local requirements and since there was no formal training, any recruit had to rely on what he could learn by pure experience in working under the surgeon's supervision. In common with seamen, whether volunteers or pressed, the sick berth rating was first accommodated in a Guard or Depot ship in one of the Home ports before being sent to sea. At the end of a sea commission he was supposed to spend a period in a naval shore hospital but this rarely happened. Staff in naval hospitals were untrained female nurses supported by male service pensioners and they resented the idea of young sick berth personnel working with them.

Invariably therefore, the sick berth rating found himself back in the Guard ship where he performed menial tasks such as ship's postman or gangway corporal, until he returned for a further commission at sea. The whole situation was unsatisfactory and required reviewing. Before this was arranged, the Crimean War of 1854 occurred and the Royal Navy despatched to the base hospital at Therapia, Constantinople, a Mrs Eliza Mackenzie with a dedicated team of nursing Sisters – the very first to be employed by the Royal Navy. As far as the nursing profession is concerned, the Crimean War brought into sharp focus the work of Miss Florence Nightingale whose magnificent nursing of servicemen was instrumental in reducing the casualty rate. Under her supervision this was reduced from 42 to 2 per cent. This she achieved by minimising the administration and insanitary conditions which she discovered on arriving in the Crimean theatre. For the rest of her life, though retired, she worked incessantly to raise the standards and status of the profession. One renowned surgeon, Sir John Richardson, who accompanied Franklin on both his expeditions to the Arctic and who spent some time at Haslar Hospital, often consulted Miss Nightingale on nursing techniques. It was not surprising therefore with nursing so much in the mind of the public, that a Committee was formed to enquire into the organisation and training of the Sick Berth Staff of the Navy and the Nursing Staff of the Royal Navy Hospitals.

Known as the Hoskins Committee from the name of its Chairman Rear Admiral Sir A. H. Hoskins, its members comprised Sir John Watt Reid MD, Medical Director General of the Navy, Walter Reid MD, a Fleet Surgeon, Compton E. Domville, a Naval Captain and Francis M. Clark, the Secretary of the Naval Medical Department. They all met in June 1883 and paid visits to all naval and military hospitals in England as well as the large London Hospitals. Naval surgeons and Sick Berth ratings were interviewed and separate opinions were sought from 'thirty experienced naval medical officers' concerning the employment of females in naval hospitals. On this same topic they had the advice of a Mrs Deeble, who was then Superintendent of Female Staff at the Military hospital at Netley in Hampshire.

All this took some time but they were able to give their report to the Admiralty before Christmas of that year. It was not until the autumn of 1884 that the Lords of the Admiralty gave their verdict in an Order in Council dated October 17 1884. This authorised the establishment of a trained Sick Berth Rating Staff and supported the formation of a trained female nursing staff for work in naval hospitals. In view of the unfortunate incidents that had occurred in the past by the employment of females, it had been the policy since 1854 to replace female nurses with male naval and marine pensioners. The verdict of the Committee was thus very surprising particularly when it was revealed that fifteen of the doctors were against the idea of their employment whilst fifteen were in favour. Obviously the final decision was influenced by the opinion of Mrs Deeble – at least that was the accepted view. This was made quite clear by the official wording of this verdict when it was recorded by the Committee that 'we are convinced that a trained female nursing staff is of the highest value to the sick and wounded and there is every reason to believe that nothing but good will result from its introduction.' So was born both the conception of trained Sick Berth Ratings and a trained female Naval Nursing Service, the latter becoming, with royal patronage, Queen Alexandra's Royal Naval Nursing Service.

The Order in Council also detailed the new rating system and pay details for the Sick Berth Branch viz:

Boys 2nd and 1st Class	9d per day (4p)
Sick Berth Attendant	1s6d per day (7½p)
Sick Berth Steward 2nd class	2 shillings daily (10p)
Sick Berth Steward 1st class	3s and 6d daily (17½p)
Chief Sick Berth Steward	4 shillings daily (20p)

All new entries to the Sick Berth Branch were expected to complete 12 years service from the age of 18 when they would receive a gratuity but if they then engaged to serve a further 10 years, making 22 in all, they would qualify for a pension.

It will be noted that by this scheme, the initial entry was as a boy rating. A continuous service engagement was first introduced for the Navy in 1853, then for 10 years from the age of 18, followed by a further period for a pension, both times being altered in the light of further experience. After the end of the Napoleonic Wars, the naval manpower was reduced from 145,000 in 1815 to 19,000, three years later. This was achieved by the release of 'pressed' men but there was the need to maintain a standing Navy in the event of a further war and the fact that there had been considerable changes in the service since 1815. Between that date and 1852, great advances had occurred in Naval gunnery which rivalled the progress from blunderbuss to the rifle. HMS *Excellent* had opened to train the new breed of 'seamen gunners' in fact some senior naval officers were convinced that two thirds of a ship's complement should be gunners. Then came steam which meant that decisions in future would depend more upon human judgement than on the whims of the elements until steam propulsion entirely usurped the former glory of the sailing man-of-war. Until that occurred, there still remained the need for skilled seamen but eventually, the stoker or as he is better known today, the engineer mechanic, would take his place. Slowly the changes came. From sail to steam, from wooden walls to ironclads and steel hulls, from the 32 pounder cannon with a range of 2000 yards, to the shell and today the missile with ranges in thousands of miles.

A complete overhaul in the way the Navy was manned came in sympathy with the early changes. Better pay was offered, bigger gratuities and other inducements as well as more opportunities for rating advancement. A new rate known as Leading Seaman was introduced thus giving the Able Bodied Seaman an advancement before the Petty Officer Rate and simultaneously, the Petty Officer was given the opportunity of an even higher rating, the then new zenith on the lower deck, the rating of Chief Petty Officer.

Such was the Royal Navy of 1884 when the new Sick Berth Rating entered. By allowing him to join as a Boy rating, it was thought that many boys from the Greenwich Hospital School could fill the vacancies. The school was part of the hospital, and taught boys whose fathers had been in the Navy. It was planned that they would leave the Hospital School at the age of 15½ and join a Training Ship as 'Probationer Sick Berth Ratings'. Personnel already serving under the 1833 scheme were to be incorporated in the new system. The boys however, were not forthcoming and their entry had to be abandoned and the Admiralty obliged to have second thoughts, particularly as they had in mind a target figure of 396 Sick Berth personnel for the whole Navy, 223 afloat and 173 in naval shore hospitals. So there appeared a revised set of regulations allowing Royal Marines who were interested, the opportunity to transfer and train as Sick Berth ratings and so as to spread the net to civilian life, new recruits were allowed to join provided they were over the age of 18 years, literate, capable of doing simple accounts and of course, physically fit. On 3 March, 1900, the following new rates of pay were announced:

Probationary Sick Berth Attendants (and Royal Marines)	1s4d (6½p) daily
Sick Berth Attendants	1s8d–2s0d (8½p–10p) daily
2nd Class Sick Berth Stewards	2s3d–2s6d (11p–12½p) daily
Sick Berth Steward	2s10d–3s10d (14p–19p) daily
Chief Sick Berth Steward	4s2d–4s6d (21p–22½p) daily

At the same three new posts were created, known as Head Wardmasters, they were to rank as naval Warrant Officers, ranks held by Gunners, Boatswains and Carpenters. This rank dated back to the early days of the sailing man-of-war and when the reigning monarch had a small number of permanent officers, sometimes called Standing Officers who maintained the sovereign's warships both in peace and war.

The boys who did not join remained at the Hospital School which was to continue long after the Greenwich Hospital had closed its doors in 1869. At that date the majority of its inmates who were reasonably capable had taken advantage of new 'living-out' pensions whilst those in poor health were transferred to the nearby Hospital Infirmary. The boys were to remain until 1933 by which time the school had expanded to include the Queen's House at Greenwich increasing the school's capacity to almost 1000. Thereafter the school was moved to Holbrook, near Ipswich, Suffolk where it still flourishes. Greenwich Hospital became the University of the Navy under the name of the Royal Naval College whilst the Queen's House was made over to the National Maritime Museum.

Unlike his 1833 predecessor, the new 'probationer' wore an official uniform on entry. This innovation was due in no small way to the influence of some of the Navy's more renowned surgeons such as Doctors Lind and Trotter both of whom were keen on the value of cleanliness and had constantly urged that all wearing apparel should be of a standard issue and washed frequently. They succeeded in getting orders for this but not until January 1857 did the Admiralty express their 'desirability' that ratings should have a uniform. By that date most ships' companies tended to dress in a similar style. The rig adopted was made up by themselves in periods known as 'Make and Mend Clothes' or bought from a contractor who ran a 'Slop' shop, a name used in Tudor times for a pair of breeches and adopted by sailors to mean any item which was 'ready made'. This unofficial uniform was very simple, a blue type of 'frock' worn inside or outside a pair of blue cloth trousers and the official issue followed the same style but also prescribed the wearing of a blue cloth collar which was decorated around the edges with three narrow white tapes, a blue coloured jacket (known as a Round Jacket) and a black silk neckerchief. Surmounting all as headgear was a straw (sennet) hat, coloured black or white depending on the station, or a blue cloth cap. Both the straw hat and cap carried a ribbon on which was marked the name of his ship but originally this was not prefixed with the letters HMS.

Many sailors believed that the three white tapes on the uniform collar commemorated Nelson's three great victories, the Nile, Copenhagen and Trafalgar and that the black silk neckerchief was an emblem of mourning for Nelson. Such beliefs were quite wrong since the tapes were used as a decoration and the black silk had a utilitarian purpose – for tying up the long hair often worn by sailors in pigtail fashion. Particularly in battles sailors would improvise methods to keep their long hair queues away from their eyes.

As for the Surgeons, initially they were all Warrant Officers and remained so until 1843 when the surgeon was granted a commission ranking with, but junior to, an executive naval lieutenant. His Mate (later known as an Assistant Surgeon) was obliged to remain a Warrant Officer until 1851. Both had worn uniforms from 1767 as Warrant Officers but in 1805 they were the first Warrant Officers to be given a distinctive uniform. At a later stage, the somewhat superior Physician was given a full dress coat of blue cloth with a stand-up collar. Both the collar and the cuffs of the coat were embellished with two rows of gold lace, each row a half inch in width.

He also had a working jacket, single breasted and like the dress coat it was fastened with three gilt buttons bearing plain anchors. Surgeons were denied such embellishments whilst their Mates were given just one uniform for use on all occasions. As well as jackets both Physicians and Surgeons and their Mates were allowed to wear with their jackets, white waistcoats and breeches which fastened below the knee. White stockings and buckled shoes completed the ensemble apart from their headgear which was a cocked hat. With variations in the types of jackets worn and the number of buttons, for a time the anchors were embellished with a snake, the uniform changed into what is almost the same pattern as today, namely a double breasted jacket with rank indicated by gold lace stripes on the jacket arms between which is a scarlet coloured cloth signifying that the wearer is a naval Medical Officer.

It will be recalled that the Hoskins Committee recommended also the employment of trained female nurses and in coming to this decision they had in mind that these ladies would additionally be employed in teaching the new Sick Berth probationers. In the early months of 1885, vacancies for trained nursing Sisters for Naval service were advertised in the following terms 'a limited number of trained Sisters of the position of gentlewomen are required for naval service'. The advert also stated that applicants had to be between the ages of 25 and 40 and have at least three years previous experience in civilian hospitals working with male patients. Two Head Sisters were also required and their age limits were advertised as being between 30 and 40 years. By 1 April interviews and selections had been made and 8 Nursing Sisters and 1 Head Sister were appointed to Haslar and 5 Sisters and 1 Head Sister were sent on their way to Plymouth.

As there had been so many unpleasant experiences resulting from the employment of females in naval hospitals, it had been the custom since the end of the Crimean conflict to replace them with males. These continued to be service pensioners, naval and marine who happened to live in the vicinity of the hospital. The replacement was slow but by the time of the Hoskins Committee's report, there is evidence to show that the replacement by males was almost complete. Very obviously with any untrained nurses, irrespective of their sex, some were inefficient yet others who possessed a measure of patience and common humanity, made good nurses. Rumours about the standards of naval nursing soon spread inevitably the bad news, hence the stories concerning what could be expected from the care of male nurses abounded. One patient of 1882 as an example stated that in the ward in which he was a patient, three males were in charge, one was extremely old and trailed around with a long beard, the second, an ex marine was an avid reader of Darwin's books and did no nursing whatsoever whilst the third, an ex-naval petty officer, was lame, deaf and partially blind. It hardly appears credible that such men could be employed in a nursing rôle. Whatever the facts may be it is certainly true that the Committee's recommendation that females should be employed to nurse the sick was extremely unpopular despite the fact that only trained Sisters would be used. In certain books kept at Haslar hospital, disparaging remarks concerning females had been written by serving naval surgeons and when the first newly recruited Sisters were appointed, they were obliged to read the comments about themselves before they commenced Ward duties. They experienced difficult stewardships knowing that they were unwelcome. Nevertheless they pursued their duties and within one year demonstrated how useful they were in raising the standards of nursing. The official report which followed recommended the extension of naval Sister's Employment to naval Hospitals overseas. The Naval Nursing Service, later with Royal patronage to become Queen Alexandra's Royal Naval Nursing Service, had come to stay.

At the commencement of the 19th century over 80 per cent of fatal naval casualties came not from battles but from disease and accident. A glance at the figures for 1810 illustrate this fact:

Men killed in action –	281	Men lost overboard	530
Men died of wounds –	150	Men killed by accidents	1630
Men lost by disease –	2592	Total	5183

The new breed of Probationers arrived at a time of considerable naval change as they were quick to learn from their seniors. Naval men for sometime were not considered with much favour by the British public who regarded them as drunken individuals and any female seen in the company of a sailor was immediately branded as a prostitute. Many writers blamed this attitude on the pay system since a sailor received his money only once in six months. Deducted from his pay were the costs of items he had received in kind during the period. These included charges for soap, tobacco and 'slops' (clothing). Also included was an item marked for 'religious' books. In the early years of the century part of a naval chaplain's pay was a perquisite known as the 'parson's groat' – a sum of 4 pence (1½p) taken from each sailor's pay on board each month. Many illiterate seamen could not understand this item and it was left to the Sick Berth Rating to explain the matter, in fact many probationers made themselves pocket money by reading and writing letters for those who were unable to do so. Another source of deduction was by allotment from pay to someone at home, usually to a wife but often the 'lady' in question was already in receipt of an allotment from another sailor to whom she was also 'married'. On one occasion two sailors from the same ship returned from a foreign commission to discover they were 'married' to the same female who confessed she had also 'married' a Royal Marine from another warship. The net result from all these deductions was that the balance received by the sailor was small and quickly disposed of in the nearest pub where yet other females awaited the pickings. When a more frequent pay system was introduced attitudes towards the Navy improved and this was aided by the great deeds accomplished by British sailors in the many 'small wars' of the late 19th century whilst protecting British overseas interests. These were always well reported in the Press and the blue-jacket made an excellent subject in action pictures by war artists, chasing slavers, hand to hand fighting the Sudanese or trundling heavy field guns into action. So the newcomer joining the branch in the middle 80's was joining a service increasing in popularity. Food too had improved. Ever since the abolition of the 'mangers', fresh meat had become a rarity but owing to a French invention of 1830, tinned preserved meat had found its way into the naval diet. The French had perfected a way of preserving meat in bottles from which the air had been removed by heating. This was copied by English contractors using tins instead of bottles, the meat compressed, heated and the tin sealed. A John Gamble, a sheet metal worker with two associates started up an enterprise and both tinned meat and vegetables were soon sampled by British sailors.

The preserved food was to general satisfaction and was first known as 'bully beef' the English pronunciation of the French name 'boeuf bouilli'. Canned meats became so popular that in 1866 the Admiralty started its own processing, the first consignment reaching the Fleet the following year. This was perhaps an unfortunate date because the issue coincided with the dreadful murder of a young lady at Alton, Hampshire not far from Portsmouth. She was a Miss Fanny Adams whose remains had been hacked to pieces and the event attracted wide publicity especially in Portsmouth where rumour had it that the new tins of preserved meat actually contained souvenirs of Fanny herself. Thereafter the meat became known as 'Fanny Adams' whilst the tin itself received the colloquialism 'Fanny' which when emptied of its meaty contents was used by sailors to draw their rum ration. This nickname has remained and is used to describe any cylindrical mess utensil no matter of what material. The water problem in ships had also improved. The sick berth man of 1833 had to be content with water that had been brought on board in wooden casks, the manhandling work involved being responsible for the many repeated cases of ruptures amongst seamen, in fact such injuries were considered almost occupational hazards. Distillation of sea water which had been recommended by the Sick and Hurt Board was gradually being introduced into warships. Nor did he have to contend with the constant earlier practice of repeated washing down of ship's decks. This had been frowned upon by surgeons as the indirect cause of chest complaints, rheumatism and tuberculosis in seamen. As early as 1830 a surgeon in a report to all naval Captains had warned them of health hazards created by this practice. He illustrated the warning by referring to his own ship in which he had served with two Captains, one who constantly had the decks swabbed with sea water and the other who preferred the dry method, namely by 'holystoning' them, a process where pumice stones (shaped like bibles) were rubbed on the decks. He explained that his records proved that there were many complaints of chest infections when the 'wet' system was used but when the dry holystoning became the practice, complaints were reduced by two-thirds. The new recruits saw also a more sober Navy, not as though the daily rum ration had been abolished, it was to last for almost another century but it had been reduced from one gill to half a gill daily. Moreover, there was a pronounced temperance drive in the Navy, led mainly by a Miss Agnes Weston, a most noble lady who devoted her life to promoting the moral life of seamen and who encouraged the building of sailors' homes offering the sailor most comforts except the sale of alcohol. The Sick Berth probationer experienced better ventilation which was a great improvement to everyone's health particularly in large warships where the air breathed by men on some messdecks had been lethal. Hammocks were slung so closely that hundreds of sailors slept cheek by jowl inhaling toxic fumes from the bilges below and the body odours from sleeping messmates. Many years earlier, naval surgeons had complained that whole ship's companies worked and slept over open sewers for such were the descriptions of the ships' bilges. Situated in the bottom of the hold they contained the ballast, usually a mixture of sand and shingle which over several commissions had become contaminated with dirt and filth from the decks above. The areas were rarely cleaned and produced fumes the stench of which was sickening. Additionally the lack of ventilation made the atmosphere humid, yet another factor contributing to chest infections. The use of pig iron instead of the former ballast mixture and the use of shunted vents for below deck ventilation had improved matters thus alleviating much of the problems. The probationer would also experience a much more benign attitude towards punishments, particularly to the naval practice of flogging a man for drunkenness, a very common offence. This was probably the most barbaric punishment where the offender was tied to a grating and flogged with a cat-o-nine tails in front of all his messmates, his bare back being torn by the repeated lashings. In extreme cases many men died, most lost consciousness and almost all could not 'hold up their heads again' to quote the words of an observer, since it broke a man's spirit.

Gradually the number of floggings decreased, from over 2000 when the first Sick Berth scheme emerged in 1833 to less than half that number by 1840. When the Naval Discipline Act was passed in 1860, the number of lashes permitted in any flogging was fixed as a maximum of 48, but rarely was this figure approached. Eventually with public and parliamentary pressure to abolish the practice, flogging faded from the list of naval punishments, the last recorded incident being in 1880 when a Royal Marine received 25 lashes. The new probationer was thus spared the harrowing spectacle so often witnessed by his predecessors who had been accustomed to dressing the weals on the backs of the unfortunate offenders.

In 1891, probationers and other grades of Sick Berth personnel were given a new style of uniform. Instead of the blue serge jumper, blue cloth collar and bell bottom trousers they received a single or double breasted longish blue jacket and trousers which were fashioned on the same style as the rig worn by Chief Petty officers. Instead of the gilt buttons and rather ornate peaked cap and gold embroidered badge worn by a Chief, they wore black buttons and peaked caps with red embroidered badges. This rig, which became known as a 'fore and aft' rig was officially issued to 'all ratings not dressed as seamen' and was worn also by the new category of 'Artificers'. These included different tradesmen, coppersmiths, fitters, boilermakers and etc, who collectively had already acquired the soubriquet 'Tiffies' – it was only natural therefore that the sick berth attendant was soon to acquire another nickname as a 'Sick Bay Tiffy'.

Yet another innovation was that he now possessed an official number and a depot. This system became general in 1872 when every new recruit joining the depot ship received an identification consisting of two letters and a number. The first of the letters indicated his depot, Portsmouth (P), Devonport (or Plymouth) (D) or Chatham (C). This was followed by a further notation which showed the Branch of every rating – J signifying Seamen, K – Stokers, L – Stewards (originally called Domestics) and M for Artificers, Cooks, Sick Berth Personnel and Stores Ratings – in fact Miscellaneous Grades all 'not dressed as Seamen'. At these Depots, a man's Service records were kept and maintained. Additionally he was always drafted to ships or naval shore establishments administered from that depot and in periods of change of appointments, he was accommodated in his depot ship whilst awaiting transfer. A Sick Berth Probationer of the 1880's would thus have received a number prefixed by either the letters PM, DM, or CM and his so called depot or joining ship was one of the many old hulks which littered the three naval home ports for many years after the Napoleonic Wars. They were decaying wooden men-of-war which were retained by the Admiralty as 'receiving ships' for new entries. A Manning Committee of 1853 had condemned them as unsanitary and added that they should be replaced by naval shore establishments but it was not until the beginning of the 20th Century that this occurred. The new Port Division system had its advantages for any man was certain that his service career revolved around his depot and in that area, as a married man, he could settle his family. It also meant that the Service had a ready source of information about every rating and could plan his career with greater ease. In the sporting field it increased the rivalry between one Port Division and another, already a growing aspect of Sick Berth rivalry between Portsmouth and Plymouth and in general, though there were disadvantages, it was well received and was to endure for 85 years.

When this Port Divisional system got under way, a short course of disciplinary training was given in the depot vessel before the probationer was moved to either Haslar or Plymouth hospital for his professional training, initially for three months only to be extended to six months and twelve months at later periods. As an illustration of timing, perhaps the following notes relating to a Sick Berth Steward named George Coker and written by him in 1916 may be of interest:

Joined 1887 in Depot Ship afloat in Portsmouth Harbour Basin
Collected hammock from Boatswain's Store
Remained in Depot Ship for training for one month
Moved to Haslar Hospital for 3 months professional training
Paid for uniform by weekly stoppages from pay
Passed examination and qualified as Sick Berth Attendant
Got Red Cross badge
Remained at Haslar for further 18 months
To Sea with Home Fleet based at Portland for 1 year
Returned to Depot Ship
Drafted to HMS *Ramilles* then to HMS *London* for 3 years
Returned to Haslar Hospital then to HMHS *Maine* for 2½ years
Returned to Haslar for Massage and X Ray course
As Sick Berth Steward selected for Royal Yacht Service
Visited Cowes, Clyde, Copenhagen, Oslo, N and S Wales, and N Ireland
1914 Drafted to HMS *Agincourt*
Signed G. Coles April 1916

These notes form a short introduction to 21 pages of typed material written by the late George Coker and describing a certain incident in his naval career.

CHAPTER THREE

The Turn of the Century and the First World War

The commencement of the 20th Century saw the end of the old hulks, the so called 'receiving ships' in the harbours of the three Home Ports and their replacements by the opening of the respective naval barracks at Plymouth, Portsmouth and Chatham. As for the Sick Berth Branch, recruiting, despite all the inducements remained unsatisfactory. Not as though naval life was particularly attractive, especially for the married man, with long foreign commissions 3 years and more away from home, although he was attached to a depot there were no married quarters and welfare facilities for his family were poor. Even at sea, though one saw different countries, living conditions were still cramped and life seemed to be one naval exercise after another interspersed with periods of 'coal ships' – detested by all or nearly so. When the collier came alongside 'boiler suits' were the rig of the day and men were detailed to descend into the collier's hold to fill the coal bags which would then weigh around 200 lbs. These were winched away to waiting hands on the warship's upper deck who would then empty the contents down yawning shutes. In large vessels the Royal Marine band played lively tunes whilst in smaller warships the men themselves sang popular ditties with added unprintable verses of their own. Everyone, officer and rating alike, gave a hand except for the Sick Berth complement who manned the Sick Bay just in case of accidents. What invariably occurred was that the Sick Berth Staff used the occasion to earn some pocket money by selling to the thirsty coal ship parties the sick berth concoction of lemonade, gallons of it having been prepared. A similar routine was carried out by the staff in ships serving in tropical waters. At a much later date the NAAFI usurped this 'perk' by opening non-alcoholic bars which acquired the name of 'Goffer' bars, the name it is thought to have originated from the Bible, Genesis VI 14. 'Gopher'. The coal ship periods were detested for they often dragged on into the small hours before the decks could be hosed. Even then, for weeks afterwards, coal dust traces still remained. Despite all discomforts however, sailors with their renowned good humour did not outwardly complain. As Thomas Holman, in his book 'Life in the Royal Navy', remarked, 'You surely get your money out of these tarry souls do you not?'. And it was more money the Admiralty offered to Probationers in March 1900 viz:

Probationer Sick Berth Attendant	1s4d (6½p) daily
Sick Berth Attendant	1s8d–2s0d (8½p–10p) daily
2nd Class Sick Berth Attendant	2s3d–2s6d (11p–12½p) daily
Sick Berth Steward	2s10d–3s10d (14p–19p) daily
Chief Sick Berth Steward	4s2d–4s6d (21p–22½p) daily

The new entries in common with other branches received some general introductory training to naval life and its discipline even learning how to salute. Before 1890 it had been the custom for a sailor to remove his cap when speaking to an officer, similarly when one officer was addressing a more senior man in rank. Queen Victoria thought this a most cumbersome process and informed the Admiralty of her opinion, so there was introduced the hand salute at first with either hand but in 1923, the right handed salute of today became general.

All these naval routines were taught to the new entry in the depot or joining establishment either in Plymouth or Portsmouth and they continued for some 3–4 weeks. Only then were potential sick bay personnel transferred to the relevant Naval Hospitals at Plymouth or Haslar, to commence the more serious side of their training. Chatham Naval Hospital, which replaced the former Melville Naval Hospital, opened in 1905 but did not take part in the Training Scheme until 1911. Tuition to a common syllabus was provided by Senior members of the Sick Berth Branch, sometimes called 'Wardmasters' because of their former duty association with a particular hospital ward, Medical Officers and Nursing Sisters both of whom had been designated for instructional medical duties. As the newly qualified Sick Berth Attendant might find himself the sole medical representative in a small warship such as a minesweeper or destroyer, great importance was stressed on the science of dispensing, instruction in this realm being given by the Hospital's civilian employed Pharmacist, usually on one afternoon weekly. All were taught how to grind the various chemicals with the pestle and mortar, how to weigh them and how to interpret a prescription and recognise dangerous drugs. On other days the class was subdivided into groups so that more detailed instruction might be given in such topics as Operating Theatre routines, the Use of Surgical Instruments, Post Mortem work, Venereal Diseases, the Care of Mental Patients and as light relief, instruction in the cooking of dishes for invalids. If such a syllabus was not enough, each probationer was attached to a Ward where under the Sister's watchful eye he got practical experience in the nursing of both surgical and medical cases and tutorial instruction from the Sister on Ward routines and Hygiene. The days were full and each month a progress test was given, the marks for which all counted towards the final selection of candidates who were to be accepted as Sick Berth Attendants and so awarded the distinguishing badge of the branch, the Red Cross set within a small circle and worn on the right uniform sleeve just above the elbow. This symbol was worn by all qualified Sick Berth Ratings and the newly formed Queen Alexandra's Nursing Sisters so that in common with all members of the naval Medical Branch, including Medical Officers with their crimson identification markings, everyone was instantly recognised from the uniforms worn. Those who failed to make the grade as Sick Berth Attendant either by not reaching the required standards or who proved incompatible to a naval community life, were returned to their receiving ships for dispersal.

Experience showed that the initial 3 month probationary course was too rushed; consequently after just a brief existence, it was lengthened to one of six months after which, successful candidates remained for at least an extra year as hospital staff in order to gain experience.

In 1902, Malta naval hospital was allowed a Head Wardmaster of Warrant Rank, and later in 1911, both Gibraltar and Portland were allowed the same. By that time the lower rate of pay for a Sick Berth Attendant had increased by 1d daily (½p) and a dispensing allowance of twice this sum was awarded to all grades of Sick Berth Stewards.

Before the outbreak of the First World War, the epidemic diseases encountered in all military hospitals were chiefly enteric, typhus, yellow fever and smallpox. In the South African War which lasted 3 years, 13,000 soldiers died from enteric fevers and almost 65,000 were invalided home, whereas deaths from enemy action were less than 8,000. Although naval personnel were only slightly numbered in these figures, yellow fever was well known. Better known as 'Yellow Jack' because of the square shaped yellow flag worn by vessels carrying sailors suffering from the disease, it had been experienced in the middle of the 18th century by sailors in the West Indies. Since that time, medical science had advanced considerably and by 1911 smallpox was under control because of vaccination whilst yellow fever was curtailed by improved hygiene methods, consequently the Sick Berth Attendant saw but few cases. With this increased progress new ancilliary medical services emerged within the nursing fields. X-Rays or to give them their correct name, Röntgen Rays after their discoverer of 1895, had been used to advantage in what is known today as Radiography with the technique of being able to photographically portray the bone structure of the human body as well as other internal organs. The innovation was quickly adopted for naval use and suitable Sick Berth personnel were trained to operate the new electronic hardware and those who became proficient received a small allowance and were allowed to wear the letter X above the Red Cross on their uniforms thus indicating their sub specialisation. Other distinctive para medical roles covered work in the operating theatre, the laboratory and the massage department. These too carried small monetary payments and the right to wear the letters, O, L or M on uniform sleeves.

It was stressed that such employment only arose when vacancies occurred and that training courses would only be available to senior members of the branch. Nevertheless the opportunities for an SBA to specialise were extra incentives to new recruits though it did not appear to make much difference to the situation for recruiting remained fairly stagnant, so yet another scheme was adopted in an attempt to improve the situation. The educational standard for the entry of probationers was lowered and at the same time, mainly to attract men in the London area, the naval hospital at Chatham joined Plymouth and Haslar in the training role and all three hospitals lengthened the course even further by making it 12 months without augmenting the syllabus in force. This meant that more time could be devoted to each subject particularly in Dispensary instruction as this had been found to be of great importance for an SBA at sea. Simultaneously with this scheme, orders were given to each hospital that probationers should not be given cleaning duties apart from the washing of patients in the normal ward nursing routines. They were also obliged to take part each morning in the Medical Officers' Rounds so that they could learn by observation of the Medical Officer and the Sister when they examined each patient. It appeared that the order of curtailment of cleaning work was in name only since all probationers found themselves attached to a specific ward and in the early part of each forenoon dusting, cleaning and scrubbing the ward's furnishings and floor remained normal routines in each naval hospital with only minor exceptions. They all had a common training schedule and a glance at the syllabus for a 1911 probationer gives a good idea of the coverage then in force. The subjects were:

First Aid
Medical Instruments
Stretcher Drill
Dispensing
Operating Theatre Techniques
Pathology
Post Mortem procedure
Invalid Cooking

Tests   Monthly as progress reports
Exams 3, 6 and 12 monthly (Final)
Grades Very Good, Good, Fair, Indifferent

The written account of a probationer's training routine at Chatham in 1911 is of interest. On completion of his disciplinary training he joined the 'Probationer's Mess' at the hospital and was then shown around his new home. The next day he was allocated with five of six other probationers (half of the intake total) to a medical ward where he would remain until around the halfway stage in the course and thereafter be transferred to a surgical Ward. The idea behind this plan was that every probationer would gain first hand experience in the routines and treatments given to patients in the respective wards. The following day he was obliged to report to his ward at 7 am where he was under the supervision of a Senior Sick Berth Steward known as the 'Wardmaster' who set him to work in dusting and scrubbing the floors. At 7.30 am, he was back in the mess for breakfast returning to the ward at 8 am where cleaning work continued in preparation for the Medical Officer and Sisters Rounds at 10 am in which he was also one of the retinue. Thereafter, he was daily employed in a variety of duties sometimes collecting medicines from the Dispensary, taking patients to the Operating Theatre or Massage Room, administering medicines to patients and on most mornings, accompanying the Ward Sister around the ward when she would elaborate privately, on the condition, treatment and progress of each patient. Breaks in this daily routine came from orders to report to the mortuary for a post-mortem procedure or to the theatre to observe a particular interesting operation. Also interspersed in a weekly routine were lectures from a medical officer on his particular specialisation, from the sister on nursing and hygiene and from the tutor 'Wardmaster' on the work of a Sick Berth Attendant at sea. Some time during the probationary period each candidate had to serve one month in one of the special departments – operating theatre, massage department, laboratory, X-Ray Department and Dispensary. If in the monthly progress tests anyone was below standard, he was interviewed by the Instructing Medical Officer and warned that he might face a discharge from the course if his marks failed to improve.

The final examinations consisted of a written paper and oral tests, successful candidates being rated Sick Berth Attendants and allowed to wear the Red Cross Badge. Thereafter for about a year he was allocated to a Surgical or Medical Wing where he did normal ward duties and then transferred to the wing of the other specialisation for a similar tour. Newly qualified Sick Berth Attendants (SBA's) experienced a 'settling in' period before commencing night duties, a duty which operated from 7.30 pm to 7 am the following morning. During day duty routines they were liable additionally for any 'special' watch duties in which three SBA's would each work a watch during the night hours in looking after any patient who was either seriously or dangerously ill. In this task they assisted the work of those attendants who were on night duty. So this cycle progressed and three years elapsed usually before the SBA got his first experience of life in a warship. Thereafter, if he wished to progress further, he was obliged to study for advancement to the next stage, that of a Sick Berth Steward, for only then could his name be put on the roster for possible vacancies for one of the 'plum' hospital courses in preparation for laboratory, X Ray, massage or operating theatre attendant. One of the complaints made by most SBA's on return to civilian life was that their naval nursing experience meant little in a civil hospital but if they had specialist experience, they had better opportunities for future employment in that capacity. Another later source of discontent was that the Royal Navy neither encouraged nor discouraged individual attempts by SBA's to obtain the qualification of State Registered status, the hallmark of a qualified nurse in civil hospitals. They could prepare for the examinations and take them but concrete assistance was not given in the way of special leave or towards expenses incurred.

As for accommodation at Chatham naval hospital, probationers of 1911 vintage, said it was adequate though furnishings were poor. Good facilities existed for sport, the probationers mess having a billiard table even though only of junior size, also good tennis courts and a cricket pitch whilst a football pitch was quite adjacent to the hospital; there was also a substantial gymnasium. As 'probationers' discipline was strict they were obliged to march to and from the hospital. They all slept in hammocks but on qualifying as Attendants they were moved to the Staff Mess where the furnishings were more luxurious with easy chairs and a bar and perhaps the most welcome change, their hammocks were stored and they all occupied beds – a real luxury.

Evening leave was given to those off duty whilst weekend breaks were operated on a three weekly cycle, one week-end from Friday to Saturday evening, the next from Friday to Monday morning, whilst the third week end was spent on hospital duties. As for food, then as always a debatable subject, most probationers of this vintage made disparaging remarks both on its quality and quantity – it appears they were eternally hungry. Some have even admitted to having eaten their specimen invalid cookery meals before they had been sampled by the Inspecting Officer and could never understand how they qualified in the subject. Obviously the officer knew their problem and was understanding and kindly.

The first decade of the new century saw the death of Queen Victoria, an Anglo-Japanese Alliance, favoured by the Admiralty as it avoided the retention of a large British Far Eastern Fleet, the 'Entente Cordiale' with France and the growing naval rivalry between Britian and Germany. No sooner had Germany launched one class of battleships than we replied with a more powerful class and as this race gathered increased momentum, it just required one stray spark to produce a momentous fire. This occurred when German armies invaded Belgium, a country whose neutrality Britain was pledged to defend and on 4 August 1914, Britain was at war with Germany. So began the First World or Great War for before it ended it was to involve most European countries, the British Dominions and Colonies and America. Preparations had been made and as they affected the Royal Navy, Reserves were mobilised. Its former Reserve 'The RN Artillery Reserve' had been disbanded in 1892 but revitalised in 1903 under the new title of 'Royal Naval Volunteer Reserve'. Together with the Sick Berth Reserves of the St John Ambulance Brigade they were both able to supply medical personnel to the

Navy on mobilisation. The latter organisation was formed in 1900 at the express request of the Admiralty. Rather like the Sick Berth Branch, initial recruiting was poor but as the spectre of war loomed larger it improved and by 1913, it numbered over 1000 recruits. Three days before the official declaration of war it supplied 850 men for naval service. To show the rapid manner of this mobilisation an illustration of the Reservists supplied from the Oldam branch in Lancashire is relevant. On 1 August 1914 the whole membership of 13 was mobilised. The next day they all reported to their naval depot at Chatham and by 4 August they were on their way to naval sick quarters, to warships, to naval hospitals at home and overseas and to hospital ships whilst two of the Party were given the rather unusual tasks of looking after hygiene arrangements in some of the gun emplacements around the British coast-line. As these Reserves had done annual periods of training with Sick Berth attendants in naval hospitals, there was no requirement for them to undertake the year's course obligatory for all new probationers and as soon as they had been issued with their uniforms, they were ready for drafts. Their uniform was that worn by Sick Berth Attendant but many of them continued to wear their own distinctive St John's uniform, a single breasted blue jacket, fastening with five metal buttons and carrying St John's crests on a turned up collar and also as shoulder flashes, whilst on their heads they wore a peaked cap with white band and badge of the Brigade. As Reserves, they also wore a most distinctive badge on their right arm bearing the words 'St John Ambulance Brigade RN Auxilliary Sick Berth Reserve'. Some, however, wore a mixture of both and it was not uncommon to see them wearing a Sick Berth Attendant's peaked cap in lieu of their own much to the consternation of Senior Naval officers. At that time as some of the photographs in this booklet will show, the Sick Berth man wore either a double or single breasted blue suit whilst those at Bighi Hospital, Malta, wore white trousers instead of the Blue. Those in the tropics, like the Navy in general wore a single breasted white duck suit, all types of jackets of course displaying the Geneva Red Cross on the right uniform sleeves.

Reserve Doctors and Sisters were supplied from the RNVR Pool of Doctors and from QARNNS Reserve Pool of Nursing Sisters employed in Civilian Hospitals. The few Civilian Dentists who had been engaged for Naval Service since 1904, were given Commissions and allowed to wear the uniform of a RNVR Medical Officer with the scarlet distinguishing cloth marking between the gold stripes of rank, the scarlet colour being retained until 1918 when it was altered to orange. As is well recorded, the First World War was to prove one of dreadful casualties in the Army with the years' of trench warfare and its great toll of lives. Deaths from disease were only about 4 in 1000 and were mainly from gangrene in wounds, trench fever and for those serving in Macedonia and Salonika, from malaria. The former toll of typhoid had been reduced by the immunisation of servicemen with a vaccine. Unfortunately in the South African War it was only available to volunteers and only 14,000 out of the 328,000 came forward. An Army enquiry of 1913 decided that immunisation against typhoid though not always completely successful was a prophylactic and so in 1914, soldiers were immunised compulsorily.

The Sick Berth Probationer's course continued throughout the War though not until the Government brought in conscription in March 1916, did the numbers really increase. In the first month of the War, only 3 probationers joined Haslar Hospital, whilst in September, October and November, there were no new entries and only 5 in the December, so the initial influx of Reservists in August 1914 was a welcome relief to the naval Medical Authorities who had many vacancies to fill. There were the new naval Hospitals at Deal and Portland and the many naval auxiliary hospitals at home and overseas, warships and the dozen or so newly commissioned hospital ships. The actual numbers in the branch when war broke out were 5000, a figure which increased to around 15,000 during the war years. In 1915, the Stationery Office published a book which was to become a Sick Berth Attendant's Family Bible. Written by George Dickenson, Staff Surgeon RN (today he would have been a Surgeon Lt Commander), it was entitled *A Manual of Instruction for the Royal Naval Sick Berth Staff*. Priced then at 1s6d (7½p) the reasons for its publication were stated as

  1: To provide a text book for probationers
  2: To promote unity of instruction in naval hospitals
and 3: to provide a comprehensive and concise manual for all Sick Berth Staff in preparation for examinations for higher ratings.

Acknowledgements were given in the Book for the assistance given by St John's Association in the descriptions for the application of triangular bandages and for their various suggestions of stretcher exercises. Containing 33 chapters in 507 pages with about 500 words to a page and copiously illustrated, it was very popular not only with naval men but with nurses in civilian hospitals.

Over the years it has been amended to include new nursing techniques and chapters pertinent to purely naval medical routines. Under the same title it was re-issued in 1930 when the HMSO charge was 4s (20p). Then in 1944 it was again revised and published as a naval book of reference, BR 888 under the new title *Handbook of the Royal Naval Sick Berth Staff* this time priced at 7s6d (37½p), since which date there have been three further revised issues, in 1959 at £1.10s. (£1.50), 1968 at £2.7s6d (£2.37½) and in 1983 at £39.70.

Though fighting was chiefly confined to land forces the Royal Navy was very much involved in convoy work, escorting our own soldiers and later American troops to all the war theatres and continually transporting food, arms and supplies from all parts of the world to Great Britain.

There were a few sea actions against the German surface units, first in the South Atlantic at Coronel off the coast of Chile, then in the area of the Falkland Isles and in May 1916, much nearer home waters in the Jutland area. In the latter action against capital units of the German High Seas Fleet, over 250 warships were involved. Both sides suffered losses ours being heavier than those of the enemy but to Britain it was a strategical victory for the German Navy never effectively ventured to sea again with a surface fleet. The German campaign then degenerated into a U boat campaign against British merchant shipping. Finally in October 1918, when the German High Command ordered their whole Fleet to sea for one final effort against the Royal Navy, German sailors refused and mutinied. The war was virtually over and on 11 November 1918, they signed an Armistice.

In all the naval tasks and in some of the Army theatres Sick Berth men were involved. There is the fascinating account of an SBA's visit to the Western Front and his time in the trenches with the Coldstream Guards and the experiences of another servicing in an armed yacht in the Channel. Such reminiscences and others have been reserved for the final chapter in this booklet.

CHAPTER FOUR

Between the two World Wars and after

1918 marked the end of the First World War from which the Allies emerged victorious but almost exhausted, especially Great Britain. The Royal Navy had played a most striking role in Germany's defeat but it became obvious at the Versailles Peace Conference in 1919 that the United States was to become the most powerful naval country of the future. Internal changes had taken place in the Royal Navy during the war some of which were of specific concern to the Sick Berth Branch. In 1918 it was announced that Wardmaster Officers of certain seniorities on their retirement would be promoted to the rank of Wardmaster Lieutenant and almost synonymous with this news was that their uniforms should carry a distinguishing coloured band of cloth on the sleeves. Details recorded in the December Navy List of 1918, described the cloth as maroon coloured, which was to remain as events proved until after the Second World War when the colour was described as 'salmon pink'. With the exception of naval Executive Branch officers who wore just plain gold stripes, all other branches wore in addition a coloured strip of cloth to indicate their specialisations. Executive officers had the uppermost ring of their rank marking fashioned into 'a circle' to quote the official wording: a somewhat disconcerting description of what became known as the executive 'curl'. This was in 1856 and in later years the diameter of this 'curl' was defined as two inches. Over the years this very obvious distinction marked executive officers in an almost separate class since they were in command of warships and its armament; in other words an apparent elite fraternity of officers which classification they guarded jealously. With the advent of steam and the growing importance of the Engineer Officer who wore the branch distinguishing colour of purple, feeling against the invidious distinction of the 'curl' and the 'colour' was accentuated. Internal ill feelings are to be avoided at any time, particularly during a war and thus every officer, irrespective of his specialisation was allowed to wear the 'curl' in 1914 and at the end of hostilities this privilege remained as by that time, the 'curl' had ceased to have any real meaning as it no longer denoted the Executive Branch of the Navy. Inter-ring colours for branch recognition purposes were abolished in the 1950's except for Wardmaster, Medical, Dental and the rare breed of Civilians officers, Constructors who only wear naval uniform when they are appointed to naval ships and shore establishments and who are in reality civil servants.

When the rankings of Warrant and Commissioned Wardmaster Officers were marked by gold rings on uniform sleeves the additional maroon coloured cloth was added below the ring and with increases in promotion in later years it was worn between the rings. Another noteworthy change in 1918 was in the title of medical officers. Surgeons and Staff Surgeons had their titles changed to Surgeon Lieutenants and Surgeon Lt Commanders, the naval rank of Lt Commander having been introduced in 1914. Other medical officers up to the rank of Admiral were to be prefixed by the name Surgeon, the name prefix being allowed to Dental Officers but their distinguishing colour was altered to Orange and they were obliged to be referred to by rank, followed by the officers name and then suffix (D). Another important change which affected the Sick Berth Branch was introduced in 1920 when the ratings of the Steward categories were altered. Thereafter a Second Class Sick Berth Steward was to be known as a Leading Sick Berth Attendant, a Sick Berth Steward as a Sick Berth Petty Officer and a Chief Sick Berth Steward as a Sick Berth Chief Petty Officer thus bringing all Sick Berth Ratings into line with the rating structure throughout all branches of the service.

The ending of the Great War was followed with a rapid demobilisation which in turn contributed to some years of depression which followed in the 20's and the General Strike of 1926. During this period, recruiting for the Armed Forces remained satisfactory and as expected with so much civilian unemployment it actually increased despite poor prospects of promotion which in the Sick Berth Branch, were not attractive. An outstanding rating could not expect more than a 2 per cent chance of being promoted to Warrant Rank during his career, although his opportunity of achieving extra pay as a specialist in the professional spheres of X rays, Masseur work, Operating theatre techniques and Laboratory work were almost ten times this figure. During the early part of the Great War the number of Head Wardmasters had increased to 6, one each in the three main hospitals, another in the Naval Hospital at Portland and one each in Malta and Gibraltar, but this number varied in the later years as Head Wardmasters were appointed to such places as the Royal Naval Sick Quarters at Shotley, Queensferry and to Hong Kong, Bermuda and the Cape of Good Hope, in fact the Navy list of October 1918 gives a total of 18 Head Wardmasters. The specialisations had increased and in the 30's included Dental Attendants and later Dental Mechanics who wore the letters D and DM respectively with their Red Crosses, and Hygiene Inspectors who were signified by the wearing of the letter H. During this period the specialist terminology was altered from that of Attendant to Assistant. The second edition of the Sick Berth Staff Training Manual, already mentioned, appeared in 1930 and like its predecessor was about the same size. Certain chapters in the earlier edition had been amalgamated in the interests of simplicity but one new chapter entitled 'Pharmacy and Dispensing' appears to have been the main innovation.

The training of the Sick Berth Probationer though now described as Parts 1, 2 and 3 training appears to have remained much the same as in the earlier years and as a brief resume was given earlier of the experiences of a probationer at Chatham Hospital in 1911, perhaps a glance at the training of his counterpart 20 years later in 1931 will be a useful comparison. He then joined his barracks at Chatham for his Disciplinary course which he undertook with ratings from other naval branches. On joining they received their kit and were accommodated in a new entry block which could hold 500 young men. Food was basic but plentiful and well cooked and was collected from the galley by duty cooks, appointed from among the new entries, and who were also responsible for the service of the meals, the washing up afterwards and the stowage of all crockery, cutlery and utensils. Everyone slept in hammocks and lived in a mess which was furnished with a table and two forms, all scrubbed white, shelving for the stowage of mess equipment and personal lockers. Nettings overhead situated in each mess were used during working hours for stowage of hammocks.

The daily routine followed a set pattern. Reveille was sounded by a bugle call relayed over the internal broadcast system – the Tannoy – when hammocks were lashed and stowed away before breakfast at 7 am. This was followed by a 'Clean Ship' routine when tables and forms were scrubbed to retain their original whiteness, floors polished and cutlery (eating irons) arranged on tables in varied fashions as one Mess vied with another. The Class was then inspected by the Duty Petty Officer acting as the Class Instructor before taking part with the whole barracks in Divisions which were held on the Parade Ground. One class of new entries in turn took the part of the Guard in preparation for 'Colours' – the hoisting of the White Ensign, or 'Good morning George' as it was known in the 30's. The Royal Marine Band added a certain air of liveliness to the proceedings and sometimes the Seaman's Band (The Squeegee band) took part. With Colours hoisted, Hymn cards were distributed whilst the Chaplain was officiating in Morning Prayers and finally, all marched off for their respective duties.

The twelve weeks training were mainly concerned in Parade work and varied from the initial stages of elementary foot movements and rifle drill with fixed bayonets, to Quick and Slow marches and Funeral Drill. The rifles used were the old SMLE 303. Two areas in Chatham Barracks were sacrosanct, the roads in front of the Gunnery School and the Parade Ground. Everyone crossing these areas had to double and sentries were conveniently posted from a Barrack Guard to enforce this rule and woe betide any rating who had the temerity to walk on these holy grounds. Whistles would blow and sentries scream abuse, even ratings on draft, loaded with kitbags and hammocks were not permitted to walk and any failure to conform meant the confiscation of one's Station Card (breathing licence as it was better known) and the appearance at Commander's Defaulters the next morning which of course would automatically mean some extra chore as a punishment.

Periods in the classroom were preceded by an allotment of time for marking one's kit. Personal names were impressed on all items with a stamp cut in a piece of elm. All white gear was stamped in black paint, blue serge clothing in white and the names were then oversewn in black or red wool. The attachments to a hammock known as 'clues and lashings' were pointed, corners of blankets were sewn down and lanyards of tarry hemp plaited to serve in lieu of pegs. They were also taught how to make a triangular plait of the hammock nettles and how to construct a wooden hammock stretcher both of which made a hammock much more comfortable to the user. Other class instructional periods covered Seamanship, mainly knowledge of various knots and splices and some instruction in Naval history. Boat pulling was carried out in the naval dockyard and in cutters with heavy 17 ft ash oars, the same craft being used for sailing purposes usually in Gillingham Reach. In this training period a good standard of drill was achieved and this was rounded off with sessions in the swimming bath and gymnasium where most probationers soon realised that when the Chief PTI ordered 'Top of the Wall Bars – GO' he really meant it as any slackening in effort meant the whole class remaining suspended from the top wall bar until such time as arms collapsed or the Chief relented. It certainly was an exacting time and it was completed with a week spent on the rifle range at Sheerness, a score being awarded to each individual and this was added to previous marks, the probationer with the highest aggregate receiving a bronze medal. Leave in the evenings was given three nights out of every four and those who remained on the fourth night were involved in sentry duties and fire parties. Finally with the completion of training, the various branches split for their Specialist or professional training the Probationers moving to the 'Boneyard' the affectionate name for Chatham Royal Naval Hospital.

They joined the Probationers Mess which contained already other probationers in various stages of their course which, when completed, was due to cover a period of 42 weeks, although a small percentage of probationers who had received special recommendations could finish in 35 weeks; a very attractive consideration as this meant sitting the final examination some 7 weeks in advance of the normal time and assuming the results were successful, a gain in seniority of the same period with a resulting increase in pay of 8s9d weekly (44p) ie from 14s weekly (70p) to 22s9d weekly (£1.14).

As with the probationer counterpart of 1911, hammocks were slung in the Mess, the hours were long and yet again complaints were made about the food. It appears that what was termed Canteen Messing was the system used and not the General Mess system as practised in the naval depot whereby all victualling was carried out centrally as well as the preparation of the meals. In contrast the Canteen system of Messing was mainly vested in the control of one senior rating who, instead of drawing the main items of food from Service sources was allowed to draw the appropriate ration money in lieu and spend it on food as he thought fit. In many cases the amount spent was kept to a minimum and any savings made were distributed monthly in cash – never a popular system from most accounts. After the previous outdoor training it was a complete contrast and restrictive to spend so much time indoors for much longer periods apparently than any other branch of the Navy under training and with a much restricted leave routine. Working hours varied in routines from 0700–1600 one day and on others from 0750–1900, from 0700–1600 and from 0730–2030. As for Weekend duties, two periods each month were spent on duty finishing at 1900 and 2030 on the alternate week end nights.

Each working day probationers were employed scrubbing the marble mosaic decks of bathrooms, sink rooms and heads and if working on an upper floor, the stairways. Breakfast followed before going to the Wards for tuition, a forenoon routine which lasted six months, the time being divided between surgical and medical wards though on some mornings the routine was varied to include lectures. The subjects covered Anatomy and Physiology, Nursing Techniques, First Aid and Poisons and Antidotes. Most afternoons were spent with the Hospital Pharmacist who tried to imprint on Probationers' minds some 242 doses of items found in the Royal Navy's 'Service afloat scale'. Practical experience was also given in Specialist Wards catering for acute and chronic cases but probationers were not sent to Mental, Venereal, Zymotic or Officers' Wards, instruction in the latter spheres being restricted to theory only. At the end of each month, reports were made by the Ward Sister and the Instructional Medical Officer conducted oral tests using the inanimate figures of George 1 (a skeleton) and his twin George 2 (an anatomical figure) to test each probationer on the male body. All this covered the first six months of the course, the remaining time being concerned with the specialist departments of the hospital, the Operating Theatre, the Massage Department and the X-Ray section. Then came the final series of examinations some written, others oral and quite a few consisting of practical demonstrations. The examination subjects were – Anatomy and Physiology, First Aid, Bandaging and Surgical Dressings, Preparation and treatment of Operation Cases, General Nursing, Service Afloat, Dispensing, Management of Hospital Wards and Sick Bays, Hospital Sick Mess Accounting, Invalid Cooking, Disinfection, Transport for the Sick and Signs of Special diseases. Additionally, because a Sick Berth Attendant was expected to give Lectures on First Aid to certain selected ratings in his ship, he was also tested on his lecturing capabilities. Depending upon the pass marks in each subject probationers could qualify professionally in these examinations as a Sick Berth Attendants (50 per cent in each subject), Leading Sick Berth Attendants (60 per cent in each subject), whilst marks of 70 per cent in each subject would qualify him professionally as a Sick Berth Petty Officer but for the latter two ratings, other advancement regulations would have to be satisfied additionally. An illustration of one probationer's results in September 1934 is shown in this booklet and, as will be seen, a special Service Form was used for the information and this was kept with other forms in the probationer's Service depot.

Though each naval training hospital worked the same syllabus there were minor variations both in presentation and technique and these differences were encouraged for they helped to accentuate the spirit of individuality in the three hospitals, a factor already stimulated by inter-hospital sports' competitions. The same feeling had already been fired by the establishment of separate Port divisions and individual Port Sick Berth Staff Associations organised after the First World War and which, in 1938 additionally, had a combined Sick Berth Staff Retired Members Association. All these organisations with their separate meetings and functions helped their members to keep abreast with changes and to foster the 'esprit de corps' within their Port Division.

International unrest that occurred in the 1930's is now well known and when in 1935 Germany was allowed to increase its naval strength to one third of our own and to have parity with the British submarine fleet, this step, with hindsight, did not help the cause of peace. Further evidence of Germany's growing Air Force was seen during the Spanish Civil War of 1936 when Germany took the side of the Spanish National Party and carried out air raids on Spanish Republican strongholds. The possibility of another war against Germany was forseen and this was reflected by the increased money devoted to Defence, to the Royal Navy in particular. In 1934 the figure was £56 million but the following year £149 million was voted. Preparations made by the Medical Department were based on the provision of personnel, the need for reasonably safe hospital accommodation and the provision of medical stores and equipment. Additional Medical officers and Nursing Sisters already on Reserve Lists could be recalled and similar personnel for the Sick Berth Branch could be drawn from recalled pensioners and the St John Ambulance Sick Berth Reserves. When war was declared by Britain on Germany in September 1939, the strength of the Branch was about 1200 but three months later over 3600 Sick Berth ratings were employed whilst the number of Wardmaster officers had increased to 43. The Government had envisaged early air attacks on a large scale on our naval ports and major cities and in the medical preparations it had been planned to provide main naval hospitals well away from Chatham, Portsmouth and Devonport. As it was thought that civilian hospitals would have their full quota of civilian air raid casualties, it was intended to improvise naval hospitals in remote areas by the conversion of buildings into shadow hospitals and in the longer term, by the erection of hutted hospital accommodation near large institutions such as boarding schools and similar establishments which could provide extensive dormitories. The plan also envisaged the conversion of merchant vessels to hospital ships for the evacuation and reception of sick and wounded naval personnel. As many ex-members of the branch will recall from personal experiences, only one naval hospital ship was in commission between the two world wars, namely HMHS *Maine*. Built in 1902 as a cattle boat, she was converted to a hospital ship during the First World War when she served under her original name *Panama*. In 1921 she was bought by the Admiralty as a replacement for the earlier naval hospital ship to bear the name *Maine* which unfortunately became a total loss when she ran aground in a thick fog on the West Coast of Scotland. After the First World conflict she was attached to the Mediterranean Fleet but on occasions detached for other commitments such as serving as a floating hospital at Alexandria during the 1935 war between Abyssinia and Italy and on a mercy mission round the coasts of Spain in 1936–38, when she evacuated refugees from both sides in the Spanish Civil War. She had certainly proved her value but as old age caught up with her, the Admiralty intended to replace her with a purpose built new hospital ship. The outbreak of the war against Germany foiled such plans as 3 or 4 hospital ships as an immediate requirement featured in the Medical Department's war plans as well as the opening of many Royal Naval Auxiliary Hospitals at home and overseas. To show the speed in the execution of this plan, five merchant vessels were requisitioned as major hospital ships before the end of 1939 and scores of new Royal Naval Sick Quarters and Auxiliary Hospitals opened each of which required both staff and stores. Moreover, with the collapse of France and the evacuation of our troops from Dunkirk it became obvious that the War against Germany and her new ally Italy was to be a long affair and its geographic spread was going to include the Mediterranean area. The National Service Act passed by Parliament in September, 1939 made all men between the ages of 18 and 41, liable for military service, and desirable as it would have been to have voluntary recruiting for Sick Berth Attendants, this compulsory entry, enhancing the branch numerically as it proved, could not be avoided. The 9 to 12 month pre-war training courses had to be reduced to cope with the increased numbers and probationer training extended to the Royal Naval Auxiliary Hospitals in the United Kingdom. Initially an abridged course of 10 weeks was tried, later to be extended to 20 weeks but as the war progressed and was approaching its climax, the course reverted to 10 weeks again. The early massive air raids anticipated on the three major naval depots did not materialise but as the intensity of the war increased air raids did occur and these disrupted training schedules but as far as was practicable every new intake received adequate instruction for life as a Sick Berth Attendant no matter where he might serve. Numbers certainly increased, by 1943 the branch could muster over 7500 including over 100 Wardmaster officers, five of whom had the rank of Wardmaster Lieutenant Commander whilst lower down the scale 90 were of Warrant Rank. These numbers had been achieved by recalling to the Service many former Sick Berth Chief Petty Officers and promoting them to positions where their highly valued services could be employed to good effect.

The 'Hostilities only' probationer was usually one of a batch of about 40 sent to each training hospital for his abridged course. As with the lengthier courses of peace time, each hospital was allowed its own training method, though a common theme applied. One medical officer was given the additional rôle as 'Instructional Medical Officer' and he was supported by a Wardmaster Officer, one or two members of the QARNNS and a small experienced staff of Senior Sick Berth ratings. The general expansion in the Royal Navy also demanded an increase in the supply of Specialist Sick Berth personnel. Qualified nurses, including mental nurses as well as laboratory assistants, operating theatre attendants, radiologists, masseurs and dispensers were not easy to find and though requests were made to recruiting officers to carefully sift the qualifications of those called for naval service, quite frequently men who appeared to have the correct qualifications were found to be useless in a specialisation. Men thought to be qualified as mental nurses proved to have worked as cleaners in a mental hospital and some who ostensibly had certificates of competence as a masseur were found to have gained the certificate from unrecognised correspondence colleges. Notwithstanding such problems, many of them proved to be excellent men and with training did show up in specialist rôles. Together with Wardmaster Officers and other members of the Sick Berth Branch they found themselves employed in almost every war theatre as it spread and in most unusual rôles-in warships, Hospital Ships, Naval Sick Bays at home and overseas, with tented units in North Africa, with the Naval Air Arm, in Iceland, Bombay and in the Tropics where special units of the Branch besides their medical duties with the Royal Navy were adept in jungle clearing, digging wells and supervising the local populations. By the end of the war the branch had grown to around 12,000 a figure which included 138 Wardmaster officers. The War exacted its toll, 327 members of the branch gave their lives and 63 became Prisoners-of-war.

State registration for civilian nurses became the hallmark qualification after the First World War and thereafter all nurses who has passed the nursing examinations and had the necessary experience were accepted as registered. Nursing Sisters of the QARNNS besides their civilian experience in the medical and surgical wards of hospitals had all passed the nursing examinations and automatically became State registered. Unfortunately for the members of the Sick Berth branch, the training given did not receive recognition even for those who subsequently had years of nursing experience in the navy and this caused much discontent to the regulars, many of whom discovered that the only hospital work they could find in civilian life was in the Ambulance Service, provided of course they could drive a motor vehicle. Naval specialist vacancies were few and even though since 1939 they included a sprinkling of jobs for those qualified as Hygiene inspectors who wore a letter H above their Red Crosses, the number of posts for which civilian qualifications were required was only a small fraction of the total complement of Sick Berth personnel. As an example the Royal Naval Hospital at Plymouth with a war time complement of over 300 had less that 50 billets for Sick Berth Ratings in specialist rôles.

The situation was further exacerbated by a limited time zone in which a member was allowed to specialise and sit the relevant examinations and it really meant that anyone keen to take any civilian examination for specialisation had to be in the right service job at the right time in his career. If he was at sea or out of the country, and from many accounts this occurred, the golden opportunity was missed. The fact that the naval training given to members of the branch was not recognised as fully appropriate for the coveted qualification of State registration was fully realised by the Naval Medical Authorities who made representations to the British Medical Association but without success. In 1942 a Surgeon Rear Admiral Falconer Hall, then the Secretary to the once thriving Sick Berth Staff Association, voiced his opinions in a letter to the Editor of the British Medical Journal quoting the cases of Sick Berth Chief and Petty Officers who after years of nursing experience in the Royal Navy could not obtain commensurate employment in civilian hospitals, but it was all to no avail.

By the end of the war apart from the numbers mentioned previously, the Navy had about 2500 doctors in uniform, over 1000 members of the QARNNS and nearly 3900 Volunteers from the British Red Cross Society and the Order of St John of Jerusalem better known collectively as VAD's. These ladies worked as nurses for sick sailors and members of the Women's Royal Naval Service, as cooks, clerks and dispensers so relieving members of the Sick Berth Branch for sea service. VAD's employed as nurses took the same shortened courses as the probationer SBA's and of course the same final tests.

With such large numbers involved in particular with doctors and men and women with para-medical backgrounds, there had to be an equable distribution of these people between the defence services and civilian population. With this in mind the Government in 1941 appointed a special Committee to examine the problems as both service and civilian organisations complained continually that their share of the market was insufficient and with the ending of hostilities, it became all the more important to release medical personnel from their uniformed service as soon as practicable. This was not easy for new commitments had arisen. There was the repatriation of so many thousands of our prisoners-of-war, some in very poor states of health, the care of our sailors employed in the 'liquidation' of Japanese occupying forces in South East Asia and the care of naval personnel who were maintaining lines of communication. Considering that within one month of the end of hostilities the Government was able to start its release scheme and maintain all its commitments showed the value of retaining the 1939 National Service Act which still meant that young men were joining the services. As far as the Sick Berth Branch was affected it was a change in name only as the 'Hostilities Only' probationer became the 'National Service' rating. Pay was improved in the July of 1946, the new probationer receiving 4s (20p) daily and 6s (30p) daily on qualifying, rates being double the amounts received during the war. The senior LSBA's pay was 7s (35p) daily and the daily rates of a SBPO and SBCPO were 9s (45p) and 10s 6d (52½p). Additionally there were new increments for Good conduct badges each worth 2s4d (11½p) weekly and were awarded after four, eight and twelve years man's service. What was even more attractive were the new scales of service pensions and the marriage allowance of £1.15s (£1.75) weekly irrespective of the number of children who then also became eligible for family allowances. A few months earlier, in line with all officer's pay, Wardmaster officers received rises.

Shortly after the War the Admiralty introduced a WRNS rating category of the Sick Berth Attendant and invited VAD's who were still serving to join the Branch. In the early 1960's the WRNS' SBAs' were disbanded and the Naval Auxiliary Nursing Service or NANAS emerged. These in turn were soon to be replaced by the QARNNS rating, and formalised Student and Pupil Nursing was introduced.

Meanwhile the controlled demobilisation continued as did the intake of National Servicemen. Many politicians thought the 18 month period of service too long and with increasing public sympathy for their views, the Government reduced it to 12 months. This altered naval plans, particularly in the manning of ships and establishments. The battleship's future, already under a cloud, was decided when it was agreed that older ones should be scrapped and the large numbers of ageing cruisers and destroyers, many of First World War vintage, despatched to breakers' yards. Then in 1948, the Admiralty introduced new regulations about certain officer categories one of which was a class of officer to be named 'Branch List' – a category of specialist officers which included the Wardmaster. In common with the other specialists affected he was to become a Commissioned officer which meant he was obliged to change his thin ring, denoting Warrant Rank, for one thicker ring signifying a Commissioned officer. It was a welcome step as Warrant Rank in the

Navy, though of great antiquity, puzzled many civilians who equated the rank to that of a Warrant Officer in the Army and RAF when in fact the naval Warrant rank had no real equivalent in the other services. The naval WO was an officer whereas in the other services he was not. As naval Warrant Officers in large ships and establishments they had their own messes but these were now closed and the new 'Branch' officers became full members of Naval Wardrooms.

As a stimulus to recruiting, new pay scales were published in September 1950 and these were far more generous than those awarded four years previously, the probationer's pay being doubled as well as the Sick Berth Attendant's and the LSBA's adjusted to 12s (60p) daily whilst proportionate increases were awarded to Senior members of the branch.

A scheme known as a 'fifth five' was introduced whereby suitable Chief and Petty Officers in undermanned branches were given the chance of serving a further five years beyond normal pensionable age, making 27 years service in total, thus enhancing pensions. A further 'sixth five' was also forecast in special circumstances.

Though the number of warships in commission had been reduced by the scrapping of many battleships, cruisers and destroyers, new jobs for SBA's had arisen elsewhere. Some of these were with the Royal Marine Commando Brigade and they began in 1946 when the Commando rôle was taken over by the Royal Marines from the Army. They were already experts in amphibious operations and for them it was a natural progression. Formed originally in 1942 as the First Commando, it was followed by seven others and in 1946 there were four remaining, three Army and one Royal Marine, then based in Hong Kong. This was No 3 Commando, under the overall command of a Brigadier RM and consisting of three units (or Commandos) Nos 40, 42 and 45, each commanded by a Lt Colonel RM. Each unit had a complement of around 640 in which there was a small naval contingent, a Chaplain, an Instructor Officer (or Schoolie) and a Surgeon assisted by a Sick Berth rating. The Brigade, better known as the 'Fire Brigade' since it could be sent anywhere at short notice to an area of unrest or the scene of a disaster, such as an earthquake, was trained for this purpose and well accustomed to emergencies.

No matter what rank or rating of the Royal Navy was involved, or his specialisation, first and foremost he was a Commando having undergone a special course before being drafted to the Brigade. In the early days this was taken at Bickleigh, Devon and of more recent date, at Lympstone, Devon. As is well known, members of the Brigade, including several Sick Berth Ratings have served with great distinction wherever the Brigade operated, in the Far and Middle East, in tropical jungles, at Suez in 1956 and more recently in the Falklands. Today's Medical Assistant can opt for service with the Commandos when he has completed his professional training. Thereafter he undergoes the Commando course before being awarded his green beret.

More versatile jobs have resulted as a direct consequence of the Second World War and because of the increasing field of para-medical specialisations. This was equally the case for those Sick Berth ratings who had achieved commissioned rank as Wardmaster officers, in fact the name Wardmaster had become a misnomer since it in no way described his versatile rôle. No longer was he in charge of a ward. He could be an administrator and adviser on staff appointments or a teacher and organiser in naval hospitals and hospital ships or in a combination of both rôles such as in the 1950's at the Naval schools of Physiotherapy and Radiography at Haslar and Plymouth respectively. Qualifications as Physiotherapists and Radiographers could only be obtained by taking the civilian examinations set by the Chartered Society of Physiotherapists (previously known as masseurs in the Navy) and the Society of Radiographers (formerly naval X-Ray attendants), just two of the new professions supplementary to Medicine. The naval schools working in close cooperation with their own and civilian hospitals provided preliminary training for Sick Berth Attendants with the right educational backgrounds to become specialists in these and other fields.

Material changes affecting the whole navy appeared in a Fleet Order on 1 April 1956. Called the 'Way ahead' it announced a new deal for the Royal Navy and Royal Marines. Just a few years previously there had been a kind of new deal when 'General Service Commissions' were introduced. These meant that warships would, in future, serve commissions of no more than 18 months at a stretch, not more than 12 of which would be overseas. At the same time all other forms of overseas service were reduced so that single and married men would not be kept away from their families for more than 18 months, assuming of course that they were serving in warships or overseas stations where families could not join them. For the Sick Berth man in particular this was a welcome change since it gave him much better opportunities to qualify himself in one of the para-medical specialities, if not for service benefit for his own when a change to civilian life appeared on the horizon. Another new deal following so quickly on the shorter engagements was unexpected but nevertheless welcomed by all the Royal Navy because of yet a further rise in pay – the third since the end of the war. In the preamble that was issued with the pay rises, the Government stated that it was their intention that all servicemen would receive pay comparable to what their civilian counterparts were earning. The Order also introduced a new form of engagement. Known as the new 'Regular engagement' it was for nine year's service from the age of 18 with no obligation to serve on the Reserve after discharge. The old CS engagement of 12 years and the special contract of seven years with the Fleet and five on the Reserve was abolished. Ratings serving on any type of agreement could transfer to longer ones and those who did received better rates of pay. Junior rates such as Probationers received an additional 14s6d. (72½p) weekly but the pay of a Sick Berth Attendant went up by as much as £2.12s6d (£2.62½) weekly and LSBA's received a similar increase whilst SBPO's and SBCPO's had increases of £3.3s. (£3.15) weekly. Increments were also awarded in good conduct badge pay, length of service pay and many other types of allowances.

There were other changes and implied changes which were not so welcome, at least to the Sick Berth Branch. One concerned the uniform worn by all Sick Berth ratings below the rating of Petty Officer, who since 1891, together with junior ratings of the Supply and Secretariat branch, had worn the Class III rig of 'fore and aft' jackets with black buttons, straight trousers and a peaked cap with a red badge. The 1956 Order changed this rig to bell-bottomed trousers, jumper with collar and a round flat topped cap which bore the name of the wearer's ship – in other words what is known as a 'square rig'. Previously blue topped caps, of all varieties had been the rig for winter months only but under the revised routine and as is in force currently, white topped headgear was to be worn at all times. The change was not welcomed by members of the Sick Berth Branch who had been so accustomed to their 'fore and aft' uniforms but as there were other compensations chiefly the dramatic pay rise, the complaints slowly diminished. Sick Berth personnel with Specialist qualifications thereafter wore their Specialist letters below the Red Cross on their sleeves and because some Sick Berth men had qualified as State Registered Nurses both in General Nursing and Mental Care, two relatively new specialisations were now featured in the specialist lettering namely N, representing State Registration and P for Psychiatry, indicating a specialisation in Mental nursing.

Considerable thought had been given to the 'Way ahead' scheme so as to embrace every aspect of naval life, personnel, pay, pensions, career prospects, accommodation, ships – nothing was overlooked. With few exceptions officers now found themselves categorised on three new lists, General, Special Duties, and Supplementary. The first concerned officers who were commissioned on entry, the Special Duties List catered for officers promoted from ratings and the Supplementary List for officers serving on short service commissions.

The Wardmaster officer featured as a Special Duties officer and on first promotion he was to be styled as a Wardmaster Sub Lieutenant (SD). He had promotion prospects to Wardmaster Lieutenant and Wardmaster Lt Commander and these ranks were achieved by recommendations and vacancies. Apart from differences in promotion prospects there was nothing in the uniforms worn by officers in any of the three Lists, rank for rank, that showed he belonged to a particular list. Wardmasters however, together with Naval Surgeons and Dental Surgeons still wore their distinguishing colours with their rank markings but this practice was discontinued with officers of other specialisations.

A much more comprehensive innovation was announced for ratings by the substitution of a Central Drafting system for the Port Division practice. This allowed a man to select a depot for family welfare purposes and by means of a method called 'preference drafting' he could select an area in which he wished to serve when due for a period of Home service. Under the previous routine he would have to serve wherever men of his rating and branch were required. The new system additionally improved his promotion prospects by giving him equal chances throughout the Navy whereas previously, prospects were confined to his Port Division and to ships which operated from that port.

There was gloomy news in the same general report regarding the future size of the Royal Navy; it was to be much smaller, more compact but better equipped. Many establishments were to close both at home and abroad and the strength of the Navy was to be reduced to around 100,000 by 1962 by which date National Service was scheduled to finish. To achieve this reduction in such a short time the premature release of many officers and ratings was planned and special regulations were introduced so that pensions and gratuities could be paid earlier and thus encourage officers and ratings who had already served long engagements to leave before these were completed. The financial induce-ments offered were generous and within two years the planned reduc-tions were made. Meanwhile naval establishments at home were closing down, others in outlying areas were moved whilst overseas in March 1959, Malta Dockyard was transferred to a private ship repairing company. Naval talk everywhere was concerned with the economies and everyone wondered which was the next establishment to close. Sheerness Naval Yard was proved to be so and in a simple ceremony the White Ensign was lowered for the last time at sunset on 31 March 1960. The whole reorganisation had been made a little more palatable by yet another increase in pay in the April of 1958 when every junior rating received an extra £1.05 weekly.

At this time an experiment was under way in the Mediterranean where a specially appointed Chief Petty Officer visited each ship in the Fleet to explain Admiralty policy to ratings and invite their criticisms. By the appointment of a senior rating rather than an officer, it was thought that more honest opinions would be received. The project was a success, so much so that in 1958 an officer and a rating were appointed by the Second Sea Lord to visit all ships and naval establishments throughout the Navy for the same purpose and report their findings back to him in his capacity as Chief of Naval Personnel. With such a large parish to cover, two years elapsed before the visitation was completed and during this interval some sources of adverse criticism had altered – mainly for the better. An illustration of this was on the subject of married quarters

– too few, was the usual remark in 1959 – but when it was explained that earlier plans for their building had been delayed by a general shortage of labour and materials and that the programme was well advanced currently with almost 9000 naval families already in quarters, most critics were satisfied that matters were improving. In every respect the team did useful work, spreading the Admiralty Gospel, listening to its critics and passing their comments to a higher authority. One early suggestion by ratings of the Communications branch was that their titles of V/S (Visual Signallers), and W/T (Wireless Telegraphists), were both outdated in view of the increasingly technical nature of their work and that they should be changed. This was favourably considered and their new title became Radio Operators sub-divided as Tactical, General Radio or Electronic Warfare, these divisions being denoted by a particular letter.

There had been other name changes, Stokers were now Engineering Mechanics and Electrical ratings, Electrical Mechanics thus it was not surprising that Sick Berth ratings wished to have their Branch title altered. It was pointed out by some, particularly those with a specialist qualification, that they had no more connection with a Sick Bay than officers of their branch had with wards.

Everyone knew that their criticisms and suggestions would reach the ears of authority and that consideration would be given to constructive suggestions. When the decision was made to abolish National Service by 1962, the Government appointed a Committee under Sir James Grigg to examine Service pay, pensions and all incidental expenses incurred by married servicemen. The Committee was requested to submit its findings with any recommendations in sufficient time for the Government to consider any implementation by 1 April 1960. The same Committee was also asked to repeat the process every two years. The knowledge that this body of specialists was at work on the vital review of all financial matters was well known to every serviceman and thus the visiting Second Sea Lord's Team was not troubled with pay and welfare problems.

In the purely medical field the war had stimulated advances in preventive medicine and naval hygiene. The expected value of a Naval Blood transfusion service had been fully justified and this was expanded post war both in the service and civilian hospitals. New drugs such as the sulphonamides and penicillin had greatly assisted treatments whilst operation techniques had been revolutionised and anaesthesia had kept pace with the demands of the surgeons. Many tasks which were formerly done by the naval surgeon were now undertaken by Wardmaster officers and Sick Berth Staff who had become experts in health physics, pathology and hygiene – factors which each supported a growing feeling that a reappraisal of the Branch was needed. Then in the November of 1965 came the news that it was to be reorganised to take account of the increasing technical content of work in the medical sphere and to attract men of the highest calibre. The title was to be changed from Sick Berth to the Medical Branch which in future was to be divided into Medical Technician and Medical Assistant sections. Sick Berth Attendants thus became Medical Assistants (MA's) whilst those with specialist qualifications were now to become Medical Technicians (MT's). The latter covered the following specialisations:

Laboratory Technicians	(L)
Physiotherapists	(P)
Radiographers	(R)
Health Inspectors	(HI)
State Registered Nurses	(N)
Registered Mental Nurses	(M)
Pharmacy Dispensers	(PD)

NB: The bracketed letters above worn on uniform sleeves were introduced to indicate new and revised specialisations, the former letter X having been discarded in favour of R whilst P replaced M for Physiotherapists and M is used for Mental Nurses.

Officers of the new branch were still to be known as Wardmasters but their new career structure included the opportunity to attain the rank of Wardmaster Commander.

The Medical Director General of the Navy in referring to the Branch paid tribute to the technical skill of its officers and ratings stating that the reorganisation was long overdue and mentioned that in future, selected members would be given opportunities to read for degrees in Science and Administrative subjects where this would be of benefit to the Service.

The 1960's proved to be years of change for the Defence Services which since the Spring of 1964 had come under one umbrella – the Ministry of Defence. No longer was there a First Lord of the Admiralty, nor a Board of Admiralty. Similar changes were made in the administration of the Army and the Royal Air Force so that the three could be controlled by a single authority, the Secretary of State for Defence. He of course was to be advised by Ministers within the Government and by Services Chiefs.

This change had occurred by the increasing interdependence of one Armed Force with another, a most apt illustration of which was shown in the recent Falkland's conflict. Though the changes were mainly in the higher fields of administration, like the ripples on a pond they had their repercussions at the water's edge. No longer did the Medical Assistant chase up new regulations in AFO's (Admiralty Fleet Orders) for they had become DCI's (Defence Council Instructions).

An earlier innovation which affected all United Kingdom civilians and some Service personnel had occurred in 1948 as a result of the National Health Act.

This Act permitted servicemen and servicewomen to receive medical treatment in Civilian hospitals, and, complementary, civilians in Service hospitals, though initially far more service personnel attended civilian Hospitals than the number of civilians who were treated by the Service but with the end of National Service, the situation did reverse. This was more noticeable in areas where a Service Hospital was situated amidst a predominantly civilian population; consequently the three naval hospitals were affected almost immediately. A balance had to be maintained and naval personnel and, with the approval of the Medical Officers-in-Charge, their dependents had and still have first priority but as the requests for civilian admissions increased, it became obvious that certain changes had to be introduced within the routines of the respective hospitals. At Haslar, extra accommodation for patients was required as well as a degree of modernisation of its buildings and offices. Being over 200 years old, the original buildings were protected by a preservation order and this created problems for the architects. They overcame them by gutting the interiors of the original buildings, modernising them and retaining the external shells thus preserving the hospital's original appearance. To increase accommodation, a cross link was added joining one wing of the hospital to the wing directly opposite. This additional accommodation comprising extra wards, operating theatres and offices as well as a new entrance to the hospital was opened officially in March 1984.

The Grigg Committee, mentioned earlier in this booklet produced two reports, after their first one of 1960, and by the time their fourth was due in 1966, a Prices and Incomes Board had been formed on the direction of the Government. They had already examined the rates of pay in various civilian trades and professions and made their recommendations, and in the light of their experiences, the Government directed the Board to take over the tasks of the Grigg Committee and evaluate Service Pay and allowances and to make any recommendations they thought were necessary. Their findings were startling for they included the abolition of many longstanding Service Allowances and the introduction of what they called a 'Military Salary'. This was to consist of one basic rate for each rank and branch of the Services, subject to income tax in the normal manner but from which was to be deducted charges for Service accommodation and food in messes – just like the normal expenses incurred by any civilian. The new rates of pay were very generous and contained an additional amount of 5 per cent of the basic pay to be known as the 'X' factor. This was to compensate servicemen for the exigencies of a service life. To minimise any criticisms on the grounds of sex-discrimination, servicewomen were to receive 90 per cent (subsequently increased to 95 per cent) of the corresponding pay of men, less the new 'X' factor. This new military salary had an accompanying effect in the life of all naval men, namely the end of the fortnightly pay muster. Unless they wished to receive their pay in cash, it was to be paid into their personal bank accounts monthly with the facility of being able to cash cheques with the ship's Supply Officer.

With the introduction of the new 'Military salary' and the knowledge that it would be subject to reviews came yet another innovation which was to affect some senior ratings, Chief Petty Officer Medical Assistants and Technicians in particular. This was the creation of a new top rating to be called a Fleet Chief, a rating equivalent in rank to that of a Warrant Officer in the Army and the Royal Air Force. The old naval rank of Warrant Officer, as held by Wardmaster Officers, had no real equivalent in the two other services and a Chief Petty Officer's rate, equivalent to that of a Sergeant-Major in the Army, was the highest naval rating. He had no equivalent to an Army Warrant Officer whose pay (and of course subsequent pension) was that much higher. This had been a naval 'moan' for many years and the Second Sea Lord's Team had been made well aware of feelings. The new Fleet Chiefs were to be employed in a managerial capacity and had to be addressed as 'Mr' by their superiors and as 'Sir' by subordinates. They were to receive higher rates of pay and obliged to serve for a further five years beyond their normal date of going to pension. To say the least, the introduction of the new rating was warmly received by all branches of the Royal Navy.

As a tribute to the Royal Naval Medical Service, in September 1970, in a special ceremony the Borough of Gosport conferred the Freedom of the Borough on the Service in recognition of its contribution to medicine and the devotion of its members to the sick and wounded of two World Wars. With a guard provided for the occasion by HMS *Excellent* and the Band of the Royal Marines playing, six platoons mainly consisting of Wardmaster officers as Platoon Commanders, Medical Technicians and Medical Assistants and under the overall command of Wardmaster Commander C. C. Hamilton, OBE, marched through the streets of Gosport to Walpole Park where the salute was taken by the then Mayor, Councillor R. A. Kirkin. It was the last service duty of Commander Hamilton who was to retire the next day. If this honour had been conferred later in the 70's the Wardmasters present would have had a different title for at long last, official blessing for a change was given. Feelings that the title Wardmaster had become outdated had been prevalent for many years received a further impetus after the change of the name of the Sick Berth Branch to Medical Branch. In the Spring in 1969, the 51 Wardmaster Officers who then made up the commissioned strength of the Branch, were asked for their opinions on a change in name. 47 were in favour and in a submission to the then Medical Director General of the Navy, this plea was made. As the same time it was suggested that prefix 'Wardmaster' should be abolished and that only the rank of an officer should be used before his name and that the latter might be followed by the suffixes (SD) (Med), representing

Special Duties and Medical Branch Specialisation. Eventually and with a slight amendment, a change was sanctioned on 15 September, 1972. The prefix 'Wardmaster' was deleted and instead of the two bracketed suffixes suggested, one new one was agreed namely (MS) meaning Medical Services, hence the top rank in the Branch became a Commander (MS).

A glance at a Navy List of the time gives an idea of the versatility of the officers' appointments. There were two Commander (MS) appointments, one at the Ministry of Defence as the Personnel Officer for the whole Medical Services Branch, another with the appointment of Support Manager for the Haslar Naval Hospital. Three of the 10 Lieutenant Commanders of the branch had appointments as Secretaries to Surgeon Rear Admirals, a further three had administrative appointments in naval hospitals, two were described as Support Managers at the naval hospitals in Malta and Gibraltar and the two remaining were respectively employed as a Health and Safety Officer and a Liaison Officer with the Services Medical Stores centre. Other appointments included that of planning officer in connection with the rebuilding scheme at Haslar Hospital, Research Officer with a 'Survival at Sea' Team working at the Institute of Naval Medicine and Administrative Officer with the Royal Marine Commando Brigade. It is also interesting to note that some officers of the new specialisation now possessed University degrees in science and in administrative subjects thus fulfilling the earlier prediction of a former Medical Director General.

In 1965 the Sick Berth Branch became the Medical Branch and was sub-divided into Medical Technicians and Medical Assistants. Both categories continued to receive the basic medical training of 20 weeks duration, after which the Technicians commenced three years specialist training and the Medical Assistants 32 weeks naval sub-specialist training. The Technician was awarded civilian qualifications as a Laboratory Technician, Radiographer, Physiotherapist, Health Inspector or SRN etc. he had restricted sea billets and was advanced by time. On the other hand, the Medical Assistant was unable to obtain civilian qualifications because there simply were none appropriate to his naval task, he had greater drafting turbulence and he had much poorer advancement prospects. With the introduction of complex new weapon systems during the 1960's, it became all too evident that the basic training 'package' had to be supplemented by the addition of more specialised 'packages' throughout the man's career so that he could meet each subsequent operational requirement. In 1969 HMS *Collingwood* introduced the Royal Naval Training System. It was called 'objective training' and although its principles were not widely accepted at first, a sign of its excellence is that each training command has now developed an almost identical system.

In 1975, the Director of Naval Medical Staff Training enlisted the aid of the Naval Manpower Utilisation Unit and a job analysis questionnaire listing several hundred tasks was sent to every Medical Branch rating. Objectives were established from this data and then discussed, modified and finally agreed with the 'users', the doctors, medical services officers and nursing sisters who were to employ and oversee the Medical Branch rating in his various rôles. Although much was done, the full impetus for change did not come until 1979 when the Training Division, Haslar, was brought under the control of Commander-in-Chief Naval Home Command and a renamed Royal Naval Medical Staff School was restyled along the lines of other establishment training schools. Objective training was introduced with the newly formed training design team producing instructional specifications with the resources a training support team could make available. Perhaps the two most notable contributions of the 1975 questionnaire have been the Senior Rates Professional Qualifying Course (SRPQC) and the fundamental revision of BR 888. Since then progress has been rapid and, amongst many other changes, the introduction of the Leading Medical Assistants Professional Qualifying Course (LMAPQC), much of which is based upon the lessons learned from the Falklands conflict and the findings of a Falklands medical task questionnaire, have been worthwhile achievements.

Objective training is not a static concept. Quality control is vital to the system. Continuous evaluation, or internal feedback from both staff and trainees within the School, provides the fine tuning which keeps the training objectives on course, whilst validation or external feedback from the users provides any necessary alterations in their direction. Thanks to the introduction of the Royal Naval Training System, the Medical Branch rating now receives packages of training throughout his career to fit him for his different operational tasks.

Part II Training

Having carried out an induction training period of six weeks in HMS *Raleigh*, Probationary Medical Assistants and Technicians come to the School for Part II training. In 1975 computer analysis of this training showed that in certain areas too much was being taught too soon and so the module was reduced from 20 to 17 weeks, mainly by transferring 'Medical and Surgical Conditions' to Part III training.

The module was further reduced to 13 weeks in 1983 in order to provide compensating reductions for the introduction of the Leading Medical Assistant Professional Qualifying Course which, by assimilating some of the subject matter, also had the benefit of further spreading the training load more evenly throughout the man's career.

Part II training is largely theoretical and the subjects covered are anatomy and physiology, nursing, first aid, NBCD training, health and hygiene, Service administration, and medical storekeeping and pharmacy.

On successful completion of this module, the Red Cross branch badge is awarded and the Medical Assistant passes on to Part III training whilst the Medical Technician starts his three year specialist course.

Part III Training

Part III training was introduced in 1965 and was of 32 weeks duration. The Naval Medical Assistant who was to be employed on general duties spent this time in practical ward training. Medical Assistants who were to join submarines, the Commandos or the Fleet Air Arm had a lesser period of training on the wards, the remainder of their 32 weeks being made up by sub-specialisation training. Unfortunately, ward training was largely unplanned with the result that the Medical Assistant was rarely moved from ward to ward to gain experience and he was often employed on the more menial, non-nursing duties. In comparison with his nurse counterparts, his training in the nursing process was inadequate and accordingly Part III training was reorganised in 1975 so that all Medical Assistants could receive 32 weeks' ward experience. Sub-specialisation training was therefore removed from the syllabus, 'Diseases and Treatments' were added but, of most importance, a clinical teacher was placed in charge of Part III training. His task was to coordinate training in the various wards and departments of the hospital and provide, in five separate blocks of one week each, the theoretical instruction necessary to consolidate what had been taught on the wards.

In addition, one week sick bay acquaint was given, a further week was spent with the Hampshire Ambulance Service, and on-job training task books were introduced. As a result of the introduction of Part IV establishment training and the lessons learned from the Falklands conflict, the sick bay acquaint was replaced in 1983 by a one week module on the treatment of burns at the Queen Elizabeth Military Hospital, Woolwich.

Part III training standards are now on a par with those in nurse training, and on successful completion of written examinations and practical assessments, the Medical Assistant qualifies for the City and Guilds Basic Medical Services Certificate and is eligible to apply for Associate Membership of the Association of Emergency Medical Technicians.

Part IV Training

Reductions in the size of the Fleet and the closure of some shore establishments have resulted in the loss of billets that were important on-job training areas for newly qualified Medical Assistants. Consequently, many could spend their first few years in the Service working in hospitals before discovering what life in the Navy was really about. In January 1983, a Part IV establishment training module of six months was introduced, the on-job training task book was revised to include establishment tasks, and during this period the genito-urinary medicine and portable X-ray courses have also to be completed.

With Part IV training behind him, the Medical Assistant is now fully prepared to serve as a member of a medical team ashore and afloat or, if selected, to go on for sub-specialisation training in the submarine programme or with the Commandos.

Sub-Specialisation Training

The specialised training of Submarine and Commando Medical Assistants is the responsibility of those Commands. However, all must complete the career courses of Leading Medical Assistant and Senior Rate level, and submarine medical ratings now also attend Pre-Joining Training Courses for service afloat. Submarine base or Commando unit medical centres are responsible for their own ongoing medical training, assisted as necessary by the Royal Naval Medical Staff School.

Continuation Training

In 1980 the SRPQC was introduced and the LMAPQC in the Spring of 1983. However, regular updating in the latest techniques of advanced casualty care is still required during the last ten years or so of the senior rate's career. As from 1985, therefore, all senior Medical Branch and QARNNS ratings will be required to return to the RNMSS every three years for a combat casualty care weekend workshop which will also requalify them as first aid instructors.

Leading Medical Assistant Professional Qualifying Course (LMAPQC)

The LMAPQC is divided into three modules of two weeks. The first is designed to give knowledge of general duties and encourage the leadership qualities expected of a Leading Hand. The second module is largely based on Falklands' experiences and covers the theoretical aspects of advanced casualty care. The final module, the practical aspects of advanced casualty care, is carried out in civilian hospitals, under the

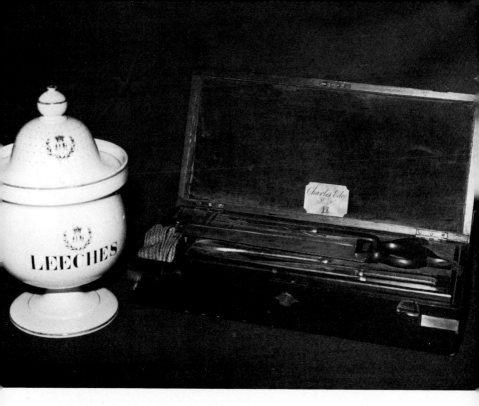

1 Leech Jar and early surgical instruments

2 Entry in Haslar's Record Book

A Complaint Lodged against Jane Brown Nurse of the Middle Center Ward Ward, for going to Bed to 4 or 5 Patients, and infecting one of them with the foul Disease. — Resolved That She be immediately Discharged. —

Adjourned to Tuesday the 24 Febru.ʳ 1755

3　Commando MA's attending street casualty in Northern Ireland

4 Inter-hospital cricket competition. 1918 winners: SB staff HMS *Pembroke*

5 A Lancashire detachment of reserves ex St John's Ambulance Brigade, 1914

S.—1237. (Established—April, 1912.)
(Revised—April, 1928.)

CERTIFICATE OF EXAMINATION FOR THE RATING OF SICK BERTH PETTY OFFICER, LEADING SICK BERTH ATTENDANT, OR SICK BERTH ATTENDANT.

......FITCH John S.N.......................................Official No.C./MX.50141 ...has this day been
†...examined by us as to his qualification for the rating of
...Sick Berth Attednant......and we hereby make the following report :—

The results of the examination in the prescribed subjects are as follows—

1	2	3	4	5	6	7	8	9	10	11	12	13	14	15	16
Reading	Writing	Arithmetic	Anatomy and Physiology	First Aid to the Injured	Bandaging and Surgical Dressing	Operation Cases, Preparation of and Subsequent Treatment	Surgical instruments, Names & Use (as supplied to the Service Afloat)	General Nursing	Acquaintance with Drugs in S.A. Scale, Compounding, &c.	Management of Wards and Sick Berths	Compiling Rough Accounts, both Hospital and S.A.	Cooking for the Sick	General Knowledge of Disinfection	Transport of Wounded	Rough Signs of Special Diseases
V.G.	V.G.	V.G.	V.G.	G.	V.G.	V.G.	G.	G.	V.G.	F.	V.G.	V.G.	G.	G.	V.G.

NOTE.—A fair knowledge is required to qualify for Sick Berth Attendant.

A good knowledge is required to qualify for Leading Sick Berth Attendant.

A very good knowledge is required to qualify for Sick Berth Petty Officer.

50% of marks are required for an award of "Fair."

Examining Officers should adhere strictly to the syllabus laid down for the instruction of the Sick Berth Staff (see overleaf).

We consider him to be..Qualified...for the rating specified.

Date.17th. September, 1934.

[signature]
Surgeon Commander
Rank

[signature]
Surgeon Commander
Instructing Medical Officer.
Rank.

Medical Officers.

[signature]
Superintending Pharmacist.

Approved, *[signature]*
Surgeon Rear Admiral.
The Medical Officer in Charge of
the R.N. Hospital at Chatham.

The Commodore, R.N. Barracks.

NOTE.—(i) When the examination is provisional " provisionally " is to be inserted at †.
(ii) This form when completed is to be rendered to the Commodore of the R.N. Barracks at the Port to which the man is attached.

N. 3976/1911. N. 892/28.

(150) Wt. 25350A/8766 1250 3/31 S.E.R. Ltd. Gp. 662.

6   SBA's certificate (1934)

7 Christmas Day, Haslar c1910

8 Operating theatre, Haslar c1910

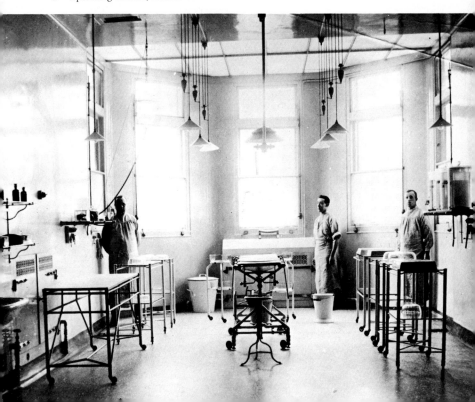

9   Sick Bay of a Victorian battleship

10   HMHS *Maine V*. Awarded battle honour, Korea 1950. She was scrapped in 1954

11   HMHS *Vasna*

12   HMHS *Nevasa* (First World War)

THE HOSPITAL DEPARTMENT AND SURGERY

13 Early etching of a
Sick Bay in a
Man-of-War c1855

control of Royal Naval Reserve anaesthetists, where they are expected to perform about 25 intubations and put up some 50 intravenous lines.

In August 1982 a questionnaire was issued to all Medical Branch personnel who had served in the South Atlantic during the Falklands conflict. It listed numerous tasks, asked how often these were performed during the campaign and how well trained they had been in the work. Of 269 questionnaires distributed, 168 were completed and returned for analysis.

Computer printouts on the questionnaire responses have been evaluated and changes in training made accordingly. In general the training was assessed as good. However, there were shortfalls in the training for the treatment of burns, smoke inhalation, casualty handling and certain combat casualty skills such as intubation and fluid replacement. All these areas have now been updated.

First Aid Training

First aid training used to be on a do-it-yourself basis and its success depended upon the interest of the medical staff carrying it out. In 1975 the First Aid School at *Phoenix* was opened and taught a standardised first aid package for which the St John Ambulance certificate was awarded. Two other first aid schools have since been instituted, at HMS *Raleigh* (1978) and HMS *Cochrane* (1981) to meet the requirements of training 10 per cent of ships' companies.

In 1981 the RNMSS was made the lead school for first aid and by 1982 the original syllabus had been completely rewritten to give four levels of first aid training – the New Entry, the First Aider, the First Aid Party and the Medical Branch rating. After nine months of validation in the first aid schools and with a post-Falklands update, the new syllabus was issued in July 1983 to all establishments and large ships carrying a medical officer.

The new syllabus is of four day's duration and is approved to Health and Safety Executive standards so that MOD civilians can also be trained. Together with newly made casualty training films, a wallet of about 150 slides and other training aids, this package will standardise first aid training throughout the Royal Navy and Royal Naval Reserve. On successful completion of all three modules by both examination and practical assessment, the Medical Assistant is awarded the City and Guilds Advanced Care Certificate and may apply for Registered Membership of the Association of Emergency Medical Technicians.

Senior Rates Professional Qualifying Course

It is at this point that the Medical Technician and Medical Assistant training programmes link together again. This five week course has recently been extensively revised with the aim of enhancing management and divisional skills and will include modules in hospital and practice administration, occupational health, instructional technique and the use of computers.

The course has been open to QARNNS ratings since January 1984 and its successful completion entitles students to a first aid instructor's qualification, and negotiations are underway to introduce a City and Guilds Practice Manager's Certificate by the end of this year.

Pre-Joining Training for Sea Service

Medical Branch ratings received no formal training prior to sea service before 1971, when the PJT was introduced. Much of this theoretical and practical instruction has now been included in the LMAPQC and the PJT course is to be reduced to one week by 1985. The new course will contain updates on combat casualty care, advice on alcohol abuse and welfare counselling.

Lessons Learned from Operation Corporate

Although the School's first priority has been the professional career package for the Medical Branch rating, much effort has also been put into other aspects of medical training in the light of the lessons learned in the South Atlantic and from a Falkland's questionnaire. These include first aid training, Royal Naval Reserve training and the updating of training films.

The first aid schools are responsible for training seagoing personnel. Each establishment, however, is responsible for training of its own 10 per cent complement and because it will take some time for Medical Branch senior rates to qualify as first aid instructors via the SRPQC, first aid instructor weekend courses are being held at the RNMSS. An additional-to-complement first aid instructor will act as a mobile adviser throughout the RN and RNR during 1984 to assist in starting establishment and divisional first aid training.

Royal Naval Reserve Training

Medical Assistant and Medical Technician training packages for the RNR follow the RN Medical Branch training packages outlined above and have recently been introduced.

From 1 January 1984 RNMSS personnel have been made available to attend the RNR Divisions to advise on and carry out the training in First Aid. Furthermore, suitably qualified RNR personnel will be invited to attend RNMSS for a two day first aid instructors course, which will enable them to carry out the continuation training in the Divisions and the communications' training centres.

The Future

The quality of training depends upon the resources and training aids available. Both the image and the facilities for training will be considerably improved when the RNMSS moves into its new accommodation in a refurbished sick officers' block within HASLAR hospital in 1985. The administration of the School and much of the routine time-consuming detail associated with training is now being simplified by the use of the new Equinox micro-computer with its five terminals. The recent acquisition of closed circuit television equipment is allowing the School to make its own 'in-house' filmlets on medical, nursing and first aid procedures. In addition, work has proceeded with the following professionally made training films:

a. *Casualty Handling*. The new film 'Handle Him with Care, Part 2' was issued to the Fleet in July 1983 as part of the new first aid package. It won the Bronze Award in the Medical Category at the New York Film and Video Festival.

b. *Breath of Life*. The original film which was made in 1980 has recently been updated and retitled 'The ABC of Cardio-Pulmonary Resuscitation'.

c. *Management of Burns, Parts 1, 2 and 3*. These films were distributed in 1978 and are at present being remade in two parts in the light of the Falkland's experience. Part 1 will show the immediate and intermediate treatment of burns and smoke inhalation in naval scenarios. Part 2 will show the principles and treatment of these conditions in hospital.

d. *Advanced Casualty Care Skills*. A training film is required to accompany the LMAPQC and discussions for a film on advanced casualty care have taken place with the British Association for Immediate Care Schemes.

Conclusion

The Medical Assistant is a unique sort of person. He is given positions of medical responsibility early in his career and, as a Leading rate, can be in sole charge of his own department at sea and is expected to be able to diagnose, treat and stabilize a patient until a transfer can be arranged. Outside the Ministry of Defence it would be illegal to teach him the diagnostic and therapeutic skills he requires to perform his naval task.

An immense amount of dedicated work has gone into improving the training standards, widening the horizons and rewarding the accomplishments of the Medical Branch rating and the School is deeply conscious of the fact that much of what has been done today would not have been possible without the preparation of yesterday – standing on the shoulders on one's predecessors only helps one to see further if both are facing in the same direction. It has, however, been a labour of love with the thrust coming from the desire to 'get it right' and nothing has been more gratifying than to hear from the 'old and bolds' the wish that they had been offered the same opportunities.

Male Nursing Officers and SLMT's

In 1982, Nursing in the Navy was rationalised and from 1 April 1983, all new entries, male and female, wishing to pursue a Nursing Career joined the QARNNS. Existing male SRN's were given the option of either continuing in the RN until their Service time expired or of transferring to the QARNNS. Furthermore male Nursing Officers were introduced, and the first man to make male history as an officer in the QARNNS was Ragendrasen Purusram a Chief Medical Technician who on 1 April 1983 became a Senior Nursing Officer.

Coincidental with this announcement was the news of a new avenue of promotion for certain other categories of Medical Technicians: this applied to Technicians in the specialisations of Physiotherapy, Radiography, Laboratory work, and Environmental Health all of whom could be considered for a new type of commission as Supplementary List (Medical Technician) SL (MT) Officers. On promotion they would become Sub Lieutenants. Provided a Medical Technician was in the required age group he could expect a Short Service Commission which could mean he would attain the rank of Lieutenant Commander before his service ended. The instruction which gave this new avenue of commissions also mentioned that candidates with the right qualifications could also be recruited direct from civilian life, and where there was a Service requirement for work in the fields of Applied Psychology and Ergonomics, Supplementary Commissions as Medical Technicians would be considered. All very exciting news and a far cry from the days when the branch had just three Warrant Officers.

Since the end of the Second World War changes in the Branch have been dramatic, its horizons have widened and are still increasing to accommodate yet new changes in the medical and social fields. The value to the nation of the training was demonstrated in the Falkland's conflict in which 220 medical assistants and technicians took part and in the Honours List which followed, one received the Queen's Medal for Gallantry, two the British Empire Medal whilst three were mentioned in Despatches. Today, in a contribution towards the Government's scheme to reduce unemployment amongst Britain's teenagers, Haslar is again featured by offering boys specialised courses as Medical Assistants and girls the opportunities to become Assistants to the Navy's Dental Surgeons.

CHAPTER 5

Naval Hospital ships and Training Hospitals

The Sick Berth Branch first received grudging official recognition in 1833 when 'loblolly' boys became sick berth men. Under this nickname they had already been similarly employed for half a century previously acting as attendants to Naval Surgeons and Surgeons' Mates in men-of-war and hospital ships. From the early 17th Century, records show that in every period of naval activity, one or two vessels accompanied the Fleet in this capacity. Books covering this subject already exist and no attempt will be made in this account to emulate what is already in print. Nonetheless mention must be made about their birth and references to those which may be in the memories of some of today's readers.

Probably the first ship to merit the title was the *Goodwill* which in 1608 accompanied a naval expedition to Algiers. This was during the reign of James I when the high esteem won by Elizabethan seamen was lost mainly due to the apathy shown by James towards naval affairs. The immediate result was an increase in piracy by foreign sailors against British Merchant Shipping. Our vessels were captured, their crews seized and transported to Algiers to be sold as slaves. In an attempt to free our men a small British Squadron which included the *Goodwill* was despatched there. The expedition was a failure but it does appear that this was the first occasion that a ship was used in the rôle of a hospital. Her Captain at the time, Thomas Squibb wrote of it as a new experience and suggested that 'Sir Richard Hawkyns may be given the credit for the innovation'. He also mentioned that the sick comforts carried included sugar, prunes, currants, mace (a type of spice), nutmegs and rice. Later, in 1654, the *Goodwill* was again used as a hospital ship in the West Indies.

From the Dutch Wars of 1852 to the Falkland's conflict of 1982, hospital ships have accompanied the Fleet but no vessel has been built specifically for such work. On economic grounds small warships are hired or requisitioned merchantmen were converted for the purpose. In the early days gratings were cut in the sides of the wooden walls to improve ventilation whilst below decks, structural alterations increased the area available for the sick and wounded.

Records show that the vessels varied between 100 and 500 tons and carried a crew from 30 to 70. Included in the complement there was always one naval surgeon, sometimes two surgeons' mates, three or four attendants and, depending upon the size and location of the hospital ship, some female nurses and laundresses.

During the Second Dutch War, when two hospital ships were in constant use, some details of the Sick Berth spare stores carried are of interest.

They included:

3 dozen	Bed rugs
20 pairs	Old Sheets
1 dozen	Pails
2 dozen	Wooden plates
10 dozen	Wooden spoons
8 dozen	Earthenware bottles

Twice as many corks

1 pound	Whited brown thread
3 dozen	Needles of several sorts

Ten thousand Pins

Broad and narrow tapes

2	Bedpans
2	Large chafing dishes
6 Pounds	Castle soap
2 casks	Brandy

Vinegar, oatmeal, barley, rice.

Fine Flour

3 cwts	Sugar; same of currants
2 chests	Candles
½ lb.	Cinnamon
3 lbs.	Mace
2 lbs.	Nutmeg
4 ozs.	Saffron

Apart from the Master, his seamen officers and crew, the medical complement was 1 surgeon, 3 surgeons mates and 3 landsmen who acted as nurses and cooks. Any recommendations made by surgeons for the improvement of the living conditions of patients were usually ignored by Ships' Masters whose personal attitudes towards all naval surgeons in general were quite indifferent.

During this period the quality of naval food was poor and complaints were many. As one surgeon wrote of the victuals supplied to his patients 'the bread delivered took the skin off mens' mouths and spoiled their gums, loosened their teeth so they could not eat their victuals' which was perhaps just as well for in a later account he added that the 'beer was often bad, flour and biscuits mouldy and weevily, beef and pork overboiled, oversalted and overspiced to conceal the initial stages of putrefaction'. It is easy to understand why so many seamen fell victim to food poisoning.

By the start of the 18th Century many naval surgeons began to serve more or less continously and on the recommendations of the Sick and Hurt Board something like an organisation arose in the hospital ship service. As a general rule patients had to be examined immediately on arrival; those with contagious diseases issued with hospital shirts; patients had to be washed daily; wards kept thoroughly cleaned, uncrowded and well aired and great care had to be excercised with hospital stores, wines and sugar being kept under lock and key.

With the establishment of sick berths in warships in the early years of the next century and the forceful directions on cleanliness and hygiene arrangements in warships by the Earl St. Vincent, the attitude towards hospital ships improved and more and more were employed. They accompanied the British Fleet throughout the Napoleonic Wars, during the Victorian era and the First World War. Probably the vessel which some of todays ex-sick berth men will recall in the *Maine*. A thumb nail sketch of vessels which bore this name and some others of similar vintage follows.

HMHS Maine I
The first hospital ship to bear this name was launched in 1887 by the *Maine* Steamship Company and later owned by the Atlantic Transport Line. She was presented to the Royal Navy by a group of American ladies who lived in London and were particularly fond of the Royal Navy. They raised £41,000 for its conversion and it served during the South African War as a base hospital at Durban. It was present at Torbay in July 1910 when King George V reviewed the Grand Fleet. Later in June 1914, she ran aground in thick fog on the Isle of Mull, off the West Coast of Scotland. Her patients were safely rescued but she had to be abandoned.

HMHS Maine II
The second vessel to bear the same name was formerly the *Swansea*. She was presented to the Royal Navy also during the South African War but suffered a similar fate to her predecessor except that she was rescued from her stranded position and sold for scrap.

HMHS Maine III
Formerly the *Heliopolis*, the third *Maine* was bought by the Admiralty in March 1913 but proved unsatisfactory as a hospital ship and three years later, she was sold.

HMHS Maine IV
The fourth ship to bear the name was an 8500 ton coal burner the *Panama*. Built in 1902 for the Pacific and Orient Steam Navigation Company, she was bought by the Admiralty in 1921 as a replacement for

the previous *Maine* and converted to a hospital ship. She was attached to the Mediterranean Fleet but was moved occasionally from this area for emergency missions such as the Spanish Civil War in the mid 30's.

By that time, it became obvious that a substantial overhaul and refit were overdue but the Admiralty was advised that this would prove uneconomic and a replacement vessel was preferable.

By 1938 it was decided to build for the first time a ship designed entirely as a naval hospital and the anticipated expenditure was approved. The outbreak of the Second World War a year later changed the whole situation and *Maine IV* remained in the Mediterranean until 1942 acting as a Base Hospital at Alexandria. Then, after a very short refit she was loaned to the Army as a carrier between the North African ports held by the Allies after the North African Landings, returning to Alexandria after a further refit and then in the autumn of 1944, she was involved in the operations concerned with the liberation of Greece. At the end of the war, the ship returned to her peace time rôle. In her most unusual career before being relieved by *Maine V*, she had cared for around 13,500 patients.

HMHS Maine V
The last naval hospital vessel to carry the same name was the former Italian liner *Leonardo da Vinci* which was captured from the Italians at Massawa in 1943 and used by the Army as a military hospital under the name of *Empire Clyde*. In May 1945 she was used by the Admiralty for service with the British Pacific Fleet and spent a long period in Hong Kong. During the Korean War (1950–1953) she transported United Nations Casualties from Korea to base hospitals in Japan. By using two decks and, on one, double-tiered beds, she could accommodate over 400 patients. Among her many facilities were an air-conditioned major operating theatre, an X-Ray department and a dispensary. She ended her operational service in Hong Kong in April 1954, where she was sold for scrap.

HMHS Oxfordshire
An 8500 ton vessel owned by the Bibby Line, she was requisitioned by the Admiralty in September 1939, converted into a hospital ship and by November was acting as Base Hospital at Freetown, W. Africa.

Apart from short periods away from Freetown for refits, she remained there until the middle of 1942. A major refit in Liverpool followed before taking up duties on the North African Coast carrying casualties between ports. Then in 1944 she entered dockyard hands on the Clyde, for the installation of new storerooms and conversion of others to an 86 bed ward.

After a short spell in Indian Waters she became an integral part of the British Pacific Fleet, sometimes on loan to the US Seventh Fleet. She next served as a hospital carrier in the repatriation of British POW's who had been in Japanese hands, returning to Liverpool in time for Christmas 1945. Statistics reveal that during her war service over 22,000 patients were admitted to her wards and a further 5500 attended as outpatients.

HMHS Vasna

Vasna before the outbreak of war was employed by the British India Steam Navigation Company as a passenger boat operating between Indian ports, and the Persian Gulf. Taken over in August, 1939, she was converted to a hospital ship with accommodation for around 280 patients. She first served in October 1939 at Scapa Flow, then in the Indian Ocean and around West Africa for part of 1940 and 1941.

1942 saw her operating in South African ports and in the transporting of invalids to Colombo and Bombay from the Seychelles and Addu Attol. For a short period in 1943 she did similar work in the Mediterranean and then joined the Eastern Fleet at Karachi where there was a smallpox epidemic. There she nursed European and Asiatic patients of both sexes, some with leprosy. Early in 1945 she took part in the landings on the Burma coast, joining the British Pacific Fleet later. She was released from war service in March 1946, after catering for about 12,500 bed patients and 30,000 outpatients.

HMHS Amarapoora

A 9300 ton coal burning vessel launched in 1920, she was requisitioned in September 1939. Besides her merchant Navy crew her medical complement included 9 surgeons, a sick berth staff and sisters of the QARNNS. Converted to carry 500 cot cases she was based at Scapa Flow until November 1942. Thereafter she was used in the North African and Sicilian Campaigns anchoring off the landing beaches at Salerno in September 1943. There she was frequently attacked by enemy aircraft but fortunately without suffering structural damage. She remained in the Mediterranean admitting both American and German POW casualties before returning to the UK for a refit. In 1944 she returned to the Mediterranean carrying patients of all nationalities between a number of ports and after a refit to prepare herself for tropical service, she sailed for the Far East repatriating Indian POW's.

For two months she became the base hospital ship at Trincomalee and then worked on hospital carrier duties in the Bay of Bengal.

When war ended, she embarked large quantities of medical stores, clothing and medical comforts for POW's in Singapore, many of whom were repatriated by the ship to various Eastern ports. Then in 1946 she carried sick and wounded Japanese POW's from Java and Sumatra to Japan. Finally, she was returned to her owners in August 1946 having admitted 9700 patients during her service.

HMHS Ophir

The Hospital Ship *Ophir* was of 4100 tons displacement with a speed of 14½ knots and 17 years old when she was transferred to the Admiralty in July 1942 by her owners, the Netherlands Ministry of Shipping. She was converted for use as a hospital ship in Calcutta. The invalid accommodation was for 350 patients and the naval medical complement comprised 5 medical officers, 1 dental officer, 1 naval wardmaster and 5 nursing sisters. She first became base hospital ship at Addu-Attol until May 1943. Then she sailed under the Dutch Flag on carrier duties in Mediterranean, work she continued on rejoining the British Eastern Fleet in September 1943. From then and until the end of the year, she steamed some 25,000 miles around the coastline of South Africa, Mauritius, Ceylon and India, transporting 3035 patients, 30 of whom had leprosy. There were brief excursions to the Mediterranean to embark Indian patients for repatriation in June 1945. Then after a final two months refit in the early months of 1946, she was returned to her owners in April. She certainly provided valuable assistance to the Naval Medical Transport organisation but the general opinion was that she was too old and too small for the duties undertaken in Eastern waters. During her service she nursed over 12,000 patients.

HMHS Tjitjalengka

Almost of 11,000 tons displacement *Tjitjalengka* was the largest of the naval hospital ships and like the *Ophir* she was requisitioned from the Netherlands in the July of 1942. She was converted to carry 504 cots and had a medical complement of 11 medical officers, a sick berth staff and 3 nursing sisters. She came into service in October 1942, transporting American and Canadian casualties to Halifax, Nova Scotia. She then became a base hospital at Freetown followed by general service in the Indian Ocean and from December 1943 to July 1944 she became base hospital ship at Trincomalee. In February 1945 she sailed for Australian waters and served with the Eastern Fleet in the Pacific and for a short period was loaned to the US Navy for their base hospital at Leyte. She then rejoined the Eastern Fleet and repatriated Australian POW's from Japan before going to Sydney for repairs. Finally she returned to the UK after embarking a full complement of service invalids from Colombo and Durban. Her war time statistics reveal that she admitted approximately 7200 patients. With her high endurance of 15,800 miles she proved a most excellent hospital ship.

HMHS Isle of Jersey

As her name might imply, she was connected with the Channel Isles, actually as a passenger vessel plying for Southern Rail between Weymouth and Jersey. She was small – 2000 tons approximately, quite speedy – 18 knots but her endurance of only around 900 miles precluded her use for anything except as a hospital carrier in coastal waters which became her employment after her requisition and conversion to carry 170 invalids in September 1939. She was based at Scapa Flow with a complement of medical officers, sick berth personnel and nursing sisters to act as base hospital to the Home Fleet and to ferry patients to Aberdeen from where they were taken by ambulance to the Royal Naval Auxiliary Hospital at Kingsmeat, some 14 miles distant. During June and July of 1944, the ship was included in the fleet of military carriers used in the Normandy invasion.

Statistics show she treated over 10,000 patients and 31,000 out-patients during her war service when released in July 1945. When considering these numbers in relation to her size in comparison with the other ships used for naval hospital service, perhaps her contribution was the most useful. •

HMHS Cap St. Jacques

This vessel was a late transfer from its French owners. With accommodation for 400 patients, after a period as a military hospital, she was commissioned as a naval hospital ship with a medical complement of 8 medical officers, sick berth staff and 7 nursing sisters. Her first trip under naval administration was with 400 patients for repatriation to the Middle East but it became evident that nursing facilities were poor and 75 patients were disembarked at Suez to make living conditions more tolerable. The remaining numbers were taken to Ceylon for repatriation but meanwhile the vessel had developed so many defects that repairs had to be done and this was only possible in Durban where she arrived in August 1945. Further delays occurred and it was not until October 1945, that the French vessel was able to return for carrier duties in the Ceylon area.

Early in 1946 she assisted in the repatriation of Allied POW's in the Singapore region being returned to her owners in April 1946.

HMHS Gerusalemne.

This vessel, a former Italian passenger ship of 8000 tons was requisitioned in January 1945 and the conversion to a hospital ship was effected in Durban. Owing to labour problems she did not leave Durban until April 1945 but trouble with her refrigeration machinery forced her return to Durban and it was not until September 1945, that she became reasonably serviceable and was employed at Manus Admiralty Island followed by spells as a relief vessel at Hong Kong and in early 1946 at Singapore. About 450 patients were nursed during her brief service.

HMHS Vita

Vita was taken over from the British India Steam Navigation Company in 1940 for conversion to a hospital ship. The work was done in Bombay and in April 1941 she commenced a short period of service which was to bring fame to her name. She had served at Port Said and from there she sailed to Tobruk to embark over 300 Army casualties all of whom were disembarked at Haifa. Returning to Tobruk to embark a further batch of casualties she found the port under heavy air attack but the embarkation proceeded. A near miss almost lifted the vessel from the sea and caused widespread structural damage and flooding and in the interests of safety, all patients and most of the nursing staff were evacuated to HMAS *Waterhen* which came alongside. It was expected that Vita would founder but though attacked by enemy planes, she remained afloat and was towed to Port Said to comparative safety. By August 1941 emergency repairs made it possible for her to sail for Bombay to refit.

Once again with her medical complement complete she saw service in the Indian Ocean, picking up 600 survivors from HM Ships *Hermes* and *Vampire* which had been sunk by Japanese dive bombers. These were landed at Colombo. In July 1942, she became base hospital ship at Kilindini, and after being relieved there by HMHS *Vasna* she carried a full complement of invalids to Durban. She remained around S. African ports on carrier duties and in the latter part of 1943 she was employed in the Mediterranean. 1944 saw her return to the Eastern Fleet with a brief spell as base hospital work at Kilindini, and apart from the intermittent visits to dockyards for repairs, the whole of 1945 was spent in and around Indian ports. October 1945 saw her in dockyard hands in Bombay before she was returned to her owners.

During her brief service, despite her ordeals, 3700 patients were nursed by the staff on board.

The Hospital Ships in the Falklands Conflict

The invasion of the Falkland Islands found the Royal Navy without a Hospital Ship, HMHS *Maine V* having been paid off from her peace time duties in the 1950's. It was thus necessary to requisition some merchant vessels as Hospital Ships in the April of 1982 and it was intended that the P&O luxury liner SS *Canberra* should be the first to be converted for this new rôle. To support her acting as 'ambulance' vessels, the naval survey ships, *Hecla*, *Hecate* and *Hydra* were selected. For various reasons it was then decided that the chief hospital ship should be SS *Uganda*, with SS *Canberra* employed as a troop carrier and surgical support ship.

Uganda at that time, an educational cruise liner with spacious dormitory type accommodation, was in Alexandria and the Ministry of Defence thought that Gibraltar dockyard was the most convenient place to carry out the necessary conversion. All appropriate departments of the Ministry of Defence were alerted, medical stores and equipment shipped and air freighted to Gibraltar to await *Uganda's* arrival which was at 5 p.m. on Friday 16th April.

The transformation then commenced and stores embarked. 65 hours later at 9 a.m. Monday 19th April HMHS *Uganda* sailed for the South Atlantic.

In that short period of time, a helicopter landing platform had been installed, a ramp added so that casualties could be quickly transferred to a lower deck reception area, modifications made to a ship's lift to allow the admission of stretcher cases and the ship's recreation spaces re-arranged to accommodate a possible 1000 casualties.

Considering the vital nature of this transformation with the additional problems of installing new power cables to operating theatres, the accommodation of naval personnel in different messes, the Gibraltar Dockyard worker's and *Uganda's* own men worked in unison like a well oiled machine. To anyone conversant with the ship in her accustomed rôle, he would have been amazed at its new appearance. Red crosses were now displayed on her funnel and hull, the students' sports deck was a helicopter landing platform, the school tuck shop a pharmacy, the hairdressing saloon the radiography department, the cocktail bar had become a laboratory whilst the students' dormitories were transformed into hospital wards. Every place had a new look.

Eighty-two medical personnel drawn from the staffs of the two naval hospitals at Haslar and Plymouth, together with 23 Royal Marine Bandsman who were to act as stretcher bearers, made up the naval contingent.

The first casualties embarked were survivors from HMS *Sheffield* and daily thereafter, injured servicemen were embarked until the end of the conflict, 159 admissions being the highest intake in any one day.

Medical personnel were also employed in SS *Canberra*, the Ambulance Support Ships, every warship, Royal Fleet Auxiliary vessels and the Royal Marine Commando Brigade fighting on shore in company with Army units.

The final composition of the Navy's Medical team excluding those at sea in RN Ships showed the following:

39	Medical Officers
15	Dental Officers
8	Medical Service Officers
15	Nursing Officers of the QARNNS
26	Nurses of the QARNNS
37	Medical Technicians
71	Medical Assistants
and 23	Royal Marine Bandsman

The conversion, equipping and eventual operation of HMHS *Uganda* was one of the great medical success stories.

In the Special Awards List issued after the conflict, the Queen's Gallantry Medal was awarded to a Petty Officer Medical Assistant and the British Empire Medal to another POMA in HMS *Endurance* whilst 3 Medical Assistants were mentioned in Despatches.

Two Medical Officers were made Officers of the Order of the British Empire and one other a Member of the Order.

Naval Hospitals

Well before the Second World War plans had been made to disperse patients in certain naval hospitals and RN Sick Quarters on the South and East coasts of Britain, to areas which were thought to be less vulnerable targets from attacks by enemy aircraft.

The hospitals regarded to be in the danger zone were at Haslar and Chatham, in fact the vulnerable area was defined as being any place situated east of a line drawn from Berwick through Nottingham and Reading to Weymouth.

When Britain declared War on Germany this plan was activated but the expected scale and severity of German Air attacks did not happen immediately, nor when they occurred were the hospitals obliged to close. Serious material damage was caused but the casualties produced were only minor.

At the height of hostilities over 100 new naval Auxiliary Hospitals and Sick Quarters had been established in the 'safe zone' of Britain which, collectively, treated over 800,000 patients during the war. The three major Royal Naval Hospitals nursed about 230,000 patients during the same period.

Significant too was the fact that at no time throughout the war was there any serious interruption in the training of Sick Berth Staff, despite the effects of air raids on the Training Hospitals.

The British public ever optimistic expected a short war, in fact many were saying it would be all over before Christmas 1939 but with the continued advances of German Armies in Europe and the forced evacuation of 330,000 Allied troops from the beaches of Dunkirk in June 1940, it became obvious to all that it was going to be a long conflict.

The medical blueprint had allowed for most contingencies not the least of which was an extension of the war and the involvement of other nations. When European countries became involved these contingencies were effected and over 70 new naval Auxiliary Hospitals and Sick Quarters were established in Allied and friendly countries overseas. Where new shore hospitals could not be opened, Royal Naval Hospital Ships were ordered to cover the areas concerned. Such Royal Naval Auxiliary

Hospitals varied from places as far as Vaenga in North Russia and Brisbane, Australia, hence many Sick Berth men found themselves in parts of the world they never expected to serve and doing work they did not anticipate, working alongside the other services or on board a naval hospital vessel in a remote part of the globe.

Peace in Europe came in May 1945 and a few months later with the Allied use of atomic bombs on the remaining enemy, Japan, the war was over. Gradually, the Royal Navy reverted to its peace time tasks but with the post war economic depression, a complete reappraisal of the future rôle of the Services became a problem to successive governments. This culminated in the rationalisation of naval resources and training commitments with the inevitable economies which followed. Certain shore establishments were shut, others amalgamated and drastic cuts were made in naval dockyards. Even the Nore Command closed in March 1961 after being connected with the Navy since 1547, which meant a contraction of naval shore establishments in the Chatham area and the relinquishing of the Royal Naval Hospital. At the time of writing only two major naval hospitals remain in Britain whilst overseas, only Gibraltar has a naval presence but the hospital's future is also in the balance.

Haslar Hospital

The building of a naval hospital in the Portsmouth Area was first recommended in 1653 by the Commissioners of the Sick and Hurt Board. One hundred years later on a 95 acre site formerly part of what was known as Hasler Farm, Haslar Hospital opened its doors for the first time. It was planned as a three-storey rectangular construction some 100 ft. wide any two adjacent arms of which were to be 570 ft. and 470 ft. respectively, the entrance being in the centre of the 570 ft. wing which faced north-east overlooking the entrance to Portsmouth harbour. By planning in this manner, an open, central 'Piazza' was left as a recreation area. Moreover this space ensured that all hospital wings would possess all round natural lighting and ventilation. The frontage was opened first and a year later in 1754, the two adjacent wings were completed but the fourth side which would have closed the rectangle, was never added, probably because of shortage of funds. By this time, Haslar could accommodate over 1000 patients though treatment in these early days was primitive and harsh.

Many patients were 'pressed men' who were always eager to escape from naval service. Those who were convalescent frequently escaped whilst those who remained within, attempted to make their lives more bearable by smuggling into their wards quantities of alcohol. In this they were aided and abetted by many of the nursing staff.

Eventually, this two-way trafficking of men and alcohol was reduced by surrounding the hospital's open ended rectangle with iron railings, 12ft. high.

It was intended to include in the centre of the missing wing, a hospital chapel and to compensate for its absence, St. Lukes' Hospital Church was added in 1762 just outside the south-western perimeter railings, access to which being obtained via a small lockable gate in the railings.

The church contains memorials to many of the distinguished doctors who have served in the hospital including James Lind (1716–94), sometimes known as the 'Father of Nautical Medicine' whose main claim to naval medical fame is in his advocacy of the use of lemon juice for its curative effects on scurvy. Through the years, other buildings have been added, a laboratory, staff quarters, additional wards and residences built in the grounds beyond the iron railings which included a burial ground towards the south-western extremities of the hospital's acreage.

As these additions increased, the whole 95 acre site was enclosed by a brick wall and the iron railings facing St. Luke's church removed. By 1903, Haslar had acquired an asylum but this was converted to additional staff quarters in the early 1960's when psychiatric patients were transferred to the Joint Services Hospital at Netley, near Southampton. Also included in the hospital was a Museum and a Library, the latter containing over 7000 volumes of rare editions of medical books and examples of botanical specimens, collected by naval surgeons who accompanied naval explorers on their early missions.

Patients used to reach the hospital by using the naval ferry from Portsmouth to Haslar Jetty about a quarter of a mile directly in front of the hospital's original main entrance. For the benefit of the sick and wounded a railway was built from the jetty to the terminus just inside the main entrance archway where a portion of the lines still remains as a reminder of Haslar's long history.

A visit to Gosport, which is very near the hospital, used to involve quite a journey by road. The problem is that a narrow inlet of water separates the hospital from the town, frequently referred to as Haslar Creek. In the early years of the hospital ferrymen plied their boats across and it is recorded that a particular ferryman was paid by the hospital to ferry hospital officials and their families to and from Gosport. In 1795 a bridge was erected to provide easier access and the hospital's ferryman found himself unemployed. Being an enterprising man he successfully sought approval from the Gosport Authorities to open a public house at the Gosport end of the bridge. It proved a financial success for the ferryman but it brought about an increase in drunkenness in the hospital personnel which forced the hospital's Governor to petition the Admiralty for the demolition of the bridge. This proved unnecessary for in 1801, in suspicous circumstances, the bridge was destroyed by 'persons unknown'. Gosport locals accustomed to the easy access to Haslar clamoured for its replacement and in 1811, Royal Engineers built a temporary foot bridge but after a few year's service it collapsed. Petitions were then received for the construction of a more substantial bridge but not until 1835 did a local contractor build a brick bridge for which civilians were obliged to pay a toll for its use. The Admiralty contracted to pay the builder £50 annually for its use by hospital officials and patients. Known to many as 'Pneumonia Bridge' it remained until the Second World War when its centre span was removed to allow small warships passage to an adjacent yard and another part was damaged during an air raid. Today, after many petitions by local and hospital officials for its restoration, a new one-way road bridge controlled by traffic lights, once again spans the gap.

During the Second World War in the spring of 1941 heavy air attacks on Portsmouth dockyard resulted in the destruction of £80,000 of Haslar's medical stores and on another occasion, the museum and library were destroyed as well as some of the hospital's residences. Fortunately by using the cellars beneath the hospital as 'Air Raid Shelters' for patients and staff, there were no serious casualties and the training of Sick Berth Attendants continued throughout the war. Figures given for the patients admitted during this time are 83,446 whilst 3248 probationers were trained, the greatest number in any year being 827 in 1941.

Royal Naval Hospital – Plymouth

Since 1928, Plymouth has been a city embracing the former separate towns of Devonport and Stonehouse. In the midst of this now densely populated area, the naval hospital was built in 1758 to provide general medical facilities for naval personnel in Ships and Shore Establishments under the administration of the Naval Commander-in-Chief Plymouth. Since the early days it has been expanded and modernised.

In the light of experience gained since the First World War, future war plans for the hospital had regarded it to be in the relatively 'Safe' zone of Britain and it was to be used as a casualty clearing hospital.

As events proved however, between the Spring of 1940 and its anniversary four years later, the hospital was to suffer from German air attacks on targets in Plymouth.

The peace time accommodation of bed patients was around 400 but this was doubled for war time and together with proportionate figures for medical officers and a female nursing complement, 334 Sick Berth personnel were required to nurse the expected patients. This latter figure did not include Sick Berth probationers whose numbers fluctuated throughout the war years as intakes varied, but despite the frequent training interruptions by the visitations of German aircraft, instruction was maintained throughout the war and 3389 probationers made the grade as Sick Berth Attendants, an average of 300 at any one time having been accommodated within the hospital.

In this respect probationers were fortunate for the permanent accommodation within the hospital which had many amenities, continued to be used and proved invaluable when compared with the difficulties encountered by other nursing staff. VAD's for example had many problems and the requisitioning of private houses in the locality was tried to cope with numbers. This in turn presented other problems particularly with transporting them from houses 2 and 3 miles away.

Air raids on Plymouth became frequent and there were especially heavy attacks during March and April 1941 when bombs fell on the hospital. One Ward block and a plaster room were destroyed, other buildings seriously damaged and the normal supply services cut.

The work done by the hospital's own Damage Control and Fire Parties in rescuing injured and controlling the spread of fires, prevented further damage. This was a great tribute to the young probationers who made up most of these emergency teams. As the hospital had its own diesel generating plant, power supplies to certain lighting circuits and medical equipment were quickly restored whilst battery operated lighting was used in messes.

On several occasions in the 1941 raids the hospital's water main was cut and as the raids seemed to occur at low water, it proved impracticable to pump emergency supplies of sea water to extinguish fires from the adjacent Stonehouse Creek. This led to the erection of several emergency water tanks at strategic positions around the hospital. One, situated on open ground between the hospital's football ground and tennis courts, held 250,000 gallons of water and it was used to quell fires caused by incendiary bombs which fell both within the hospital and on the nearby civilian homes.

When air raids severed the gas mains supplying the hospitals' cooking systems, the diesel operated range in the SB Staff Quarters, together with portable stoves of Army pattern, provided the cooking facilities for patients who despite all the hardships involved managed to receive adequate diets.

Local civilian air raid casulties were admitted to the hospital but where convalescence was involved, patients were transferred to the RN Auxiliary Hospitals at Maristoe, Newton Abbot and Barrow Gurney. The provision of ambulances and other forms of transport was quite a large problem and this section of the hospital's work was enlarged during the course of the war. Working parties of probationers were used throughout as stretcher bearers for all cases transported. Besides the conventional ambulances, bus type vehicles were added to the ambulance fleet and each week an ambulance railway coach was used to transfer patients and their baggage to the Auxiliary hospitals at Newton Abbot and Barrow Gurney. This coach was a GWR Dining Car, re-equipped to carry 8 cot cases and 12 non-cot patients and in the days of acute petrol shortages, it was a great boom.

The hospital records show that in spite of the 602 Air Raids on Plymouth from July 1940 to April 1944 and the great strain it had on the hospital staff, over 60,000 patients were admitted and a further 30,000 annually were treated as out-patients before the war ended.

As with the other major naval hospitals, the 1948 Health Acts allowed naval hospitals to admit both civilian and service patients, as a reciprocal facility to that afforded by civilian hospitals. Over the years a balance has been struck both at Plymouth and Haslar where the percentage of civilian patients appears to have settled at 70% a figure which includes the dependants of servicemen.

Barrow Gurney – RN Auxiliary Hospital

In March 1939, the Ministry of Health agreed with the Admiralty that the Barrow Gurney Mental Hospital some 5 miles outside Bristol could be transferred to Naval control as an Auxiliary Hospital in the event of war.

Situated as hospital blocks, widely separated in extensive wooded grounds on a secondary road approached either from Bristol or Bridgewater, it accommodated 500 mental patients. It was taken over by the Royal Navy in August 1939, equipped and staffed by doctors and nursing staff including almost 200 sick berth personnel, to cater for naval patients with mental disorders. The medical officers included consultants in neurology, neuro-surgery and psychological medicine. Because of facilities already available and the spacious nature of its accommodation, all staff lived within the hospital.

Although patients were admitted to the hospital from 1939 until 1946, it was not until July 1942 that the hospital undertook the training of probationers for entry as sick berth attendants. The Wardmaster Officer chosen for this training rôle was specially selected for the appointment and he was allowed to choose his own staff which consisted of 3 Sick Berth Chief Petty Officers, 2 Sick Berth Petty Officers and 2 Leading Sick Berth Attendants who were mainly concerned with routine office work. Although within the confines of the Auxiliary Hospital and under the overall supervision of an Instructional Medical Officer who was a specialist doctor on the hospital staff, this Training Section was quite separate. The probationers were accommodated in Nissen type huts which, with lecture halls, dining halls, kitchen and washing facilities, formed a self contained unit within the hospital's spacious grounds. The capacity was 200 probationers under training at any one time and they arrived at 5 weekly intervals, 50 on each occasion. The course undertaken lasted 20 weeks but as the standard of probationers received during the war years varied considerably, the pass rate was only 70 per cent. The first class arrived in July 1942 and the training continued until July 1946 when the section finally closed.

The actual figures covering the whole period of its operation were recorded as:

Staff   2 Medical Officers
           1 Warrant Wardmaster Officer
           5 Senior Sick Berth Personnel
         18 Junior Sick Berth Attendants
         14 Civilian Staff
           2 W.R.N.S.
Probationers under training 1595
Those who qualified as SBA's 1198

Successful probationers were drafted to the Portsmouth and Chatham depots for eventual disposal to Ships and Shore Establishments under their respective administrations.

Royal Naval Auxiliary Hospital – Kingseat

Brief mention was made earlier to HMHS *Isle of Jersey* which from September 1939 was based at Scapa Flow and which was used to ferry patients from the Home Fleet to Aberdeen for onward transport to the RN Auxiliary Hospital at Kingseat, 14 miles distant. From September 1939, Kingseat Mental Institution was evacuated of its patients and transferred to naval administration.

Situated, North West of Aberdeen and 500 ft. above sea level, Kingseat had been carefully earmarked by the Admiralty in the event of war because of its facilities, namely of providing a large medical establishment sufficiently remote from populated areas to be relatively safe from air attacks.

The 800 mental patients which it nursed pre-war were transferred to other institutions by mid September 1939 by which time the hospital was ready to admit up to 250 Service patients. Many alterations were made within the hospital to accommodate larger numbers and Sick Berth Pensioners were recalled for Service to ensure sufficient staff to cater for any sudden large influx of casualties from the Fleet.

In 1943, an Instructional Department was instituted and the training of large numbers of probationers undertaken. With a theatre seating 500 and equipped with modern stage lighting, there were twice weekly cinema shows as well as live entertainment by ENSA touring parties, Kingseat was probably the most popular of all training hospitals.

Hospital wise, it received over 37,000 patients during the Second World War.

Royal Naval Hospital Chatham

Both the old naval hospitals at Haslar and Plymouth consist of buildings, some quite isolated which are spread over large areas. In comparison, the Royal Navy Hospital, Chatham, now sadly no longer under naval administration, was relatively modern. Opened in 1905 by King Edward VII, isolation was avoided by the construction of a single building built around a central wide corridor from which, with minor exceptions, all hospital departments could be reached. The exceptions were isolation wards, the hospital's church and staff accommodation.

With a peace time accommodation for around 750 beds, at the outbreak of the Second World War the number of beds was increased to 850. Because of its situation just a mile from Chatham dockyard and on the direct flight path of aircraft approaching London from the Continent via the Thames Estuary, the hospital was a most vulnerable target during the war.

For this reason, apart from the increased bed provision and the possibility that at some stage in the war the hospital might become untenable, provision was made with the London County Council Southern Hospital at Dartford, 20 miles away to accept large numbers of service patients. Naval doctors and Sick Berth Staff were appointed to a naval wing of Dartford hospital for this purpose. The result was that throughout the war, the RNH Chatham was never particularly strained at anytime as patients were transferred thus leaving available up to 400 beds for the reception of emergency casualties. The training of Sick Berth Probationers was first undertaken in 1911 and continued through both world wars but during the second conflict, the total Sick Berth Staff including probationers never exceeded 400, just twice the number borne in pre-Second World War days.

Throughout the war, accommodation for the staff was a problem and despite the conversion of the recreation room and gymnasium into dormitories, there was gross overcrowding.

Passive defence against air raids meant the blacking out of over 8000 windows and the construction of shelters both in the hospital's basements and grounds, to which all except severely ill patients were removed during air raids. Those too ill or handicapped to be transferred were always accommodated in ground floor wards.

Bombs were dropped on many occasions in the neighbourhood of the hospital throughout the war years but the buildings themselves were undamaged.

86,205 patients passed through the hospital during the war, a figure which exceeds by around 3000, the number recorded by any other Naval hospital.

With the economies that occurred in the Navy after the Second World War, the Nore Command was severely affected. The former Royal Marine Barracks at Chatham and the Naval Gun Wharf had been sold to a private firm in 1959 whilst the Nore Command itself formally ended in March 1961, the Royal Naval Hospital Chatham closing for naval use in the same year.

CHAPTER SIX

Orders Decorations and Medals to the Sick Berth and Medical Branch Staff

Introduction

Honours and Awards

After the First World War Sick Berth Associations were formed in each of the three naval home ports mainly to help those leaving the service to find suitable civilian employment but as might be expected, the Associations also became a centre for social events. Because of their popularity, a separate Association was formed in 1938 for retired personnel of the Branch and by 1950 it numbered over 700.

Unfortunately, by that date the number of members in the original societies had dwindled and it became obvious that unless some new stimulus occurred to recruiting, the port associations would have to be disbanded. By 1966 this happened and by throwing open membership to serving members as well as retired, it was thought that the retired members' association might increase in numbers as it too had declined in popularity. Accordingly in 1966, its name was changed to the Royal Naval Sick Berth Staff and Retired Members' Association. Only a few new members were forthcoming however and by 1971, the once buoyant Association was reduced to a mere 60 paid up members. An extraordinary meeting of its officials was called in the April of that year and it was decided that if numbers continued to fall, the Association could not continue. By the time of the AGM in the November 1981 when numbers had fallen still further, the Society decided to wind up its affairs. Outstanding debts were paid and the remaining balance of around £300 was presented to the Royal Naval Benevolent Trust for the funds of Pembroke House, Gillingham, Kent. The Acting Secretary of the Association at that time and for many years previously was a Jack Fitch who had served in the Sick Berth Branch from 1933–47 and who in civilian life had always kept in touch with changes in the Branch and knew much of its history. Contact was made with him and the information given in this chapter has been supplied by his research work. He does make the point that the lists given may not be complete which is his ultimate aim and would like readers who are aware of any omissions etc, to send details of these to the:

Curator and Librarian
RN Hospital
Haslar Hospital
Gosport
Hants

who is keeping the archival material relating to the former Sick Berth Branch of the RN and its successor, the Medical Branch.

Order of Precedence

The Most Excellent Order of the British Empire ranks sixth out of the Orders of Chivalry of the United Kingdom.

Orders decorations and medals, and their ribbands are worn in the following order.

OBE
MBE
ARRC
Albert Medal. (Now exchanged for the George Cross)
Conspicuous Gallantry Medal
George Medal
Distinguished Service Medal
Queen's Gallantry Medal
British Empire Medal
Campaign Medals in chronological order and bearing oak leaves for any mentions in Despatches or commendations. If no medal is granted these are worn separately after any other ribbands.

The following abbreviations are used in this chapter:

SBR	Sick Berth Reserve
PSBA	Probationary Sick Berth Attendant
SBA	Sick Berth Attendant
SBS	Sick Berth Steward
LSBA	Leading Sick Berth Attendant
SBPO	Sick Berth Petty Officer
SBCPO	Sick Berth Chief Petty Officer
Ch SBS	Chief Sick Berth Steward
SRA	Senior Reserve Attendant
PMA	Probationary Medical Assistant
MA	Medical Assistant
LMA	Leading Medical Assistant
POMA	Petty Officer Medical Assistant
CPOMA	Chief Petty Officer Medical Assistant
FCMA	Fleet Chief Medical Assistant
MT	Medical Technician
POMT	Petty Officer Medical Technician
CMT	Chief Petty Officer Medical Technician
FCMT	Fleet Chief Medical Technician

RAN	Royal Australian Navy
RNZN	Royal New Zealand Navy
RCN	Royal Canadian Navy
RCNVR	Royal Canadian Navy Volunteer Reserve
RNVR	Royal Naval Volunteer Reserve
RIN	Royal Indian Navy
CH	Chatham Division
DEV	Devonport or Plymouth Division
PO	Portsmouth Division
DSM	Distinguished Service Medal
QGM	Queen's Gallantry Medal
OBE	Officer of the Most Excellent Order of the British Empire
MBE	Member of the Most Excellent Order of the British Empire
BEM	Medal of the Most Excellent Order of the British Empire
AM	Albert Medal (now replaced by the George Cross (GC))
CGM	Conspicuous Gallantry Medal (now replaced by the George Cross)
GC	George Cross
GM	George Medal
ARRC	Associate of the Order of the Royal Red Cross

The Most Excellent Order of the British Empire

The Order was founded in 1917 by King George the Fifth as an award divided into five classes and open to men and women. It was announced officially in the following manner:

At the Court of Buckingham Palace, 27th December 1918.

The King has been graciously pleased to institute the Military Division of The Most Excellent Order of the British Empire to date from the creation of the Order i.e. from 4th June 1917. The following classes of persons will be eligible for appointment to the Military Division of the Order.

All Commissioned, Warrant and subordinate Officers subject to the Naval Discipline Act, employed under order of Admiralty, and all Commissioned and Warrant Officers, recommended by any C in C, all members of Naval Army Dominions or Overseas Nursing Services, and officials or WRNS.

The insignia of both Military and Civil Divisions will be the same, but the Military Division will be distinguished by the vertical red stripe in centre of the existing ribbon.

The five classes of the Order are:

Knights (or Dames) Grand Cross	GBE
Knights (or Dames) Commanders	KBE or DBE

Commanders	CBE
Officers	OBE
Members	MBE

There is also a medal of the Order known as the BEM.
Until 1940 an Empire Gallantry medal was issued. This was replaced by the George Cross.

The original insignia bore the head of Britannia in the centre, but in 1937 this was changed to the crowned Heads of Queen Mary and King George the Fifth. At the same time the original ribbon of purple with red edges and strips (MIL) was changed for a rose pink ribbon with pearl grey edges and stripes (MIL).

British Empire Medal (Military)

The BEM may be awarded to Petty Officers and Men of the Royal Navy or NCO's and Men of the Royal Marines or to Nursing Members of the Voluntary Aid Detachment who belong to one of the officially recognised Nursing Services, or have voluntarily undertaken nursing duties, for gallantry or distinguished conduct not in the face of the enemy whether on shore or at sea, or for meritorious service over a period either ashore or afloat. The Medal may also be awarded for services in action against the enemy.

It carries the right to use the initials BEM after one's surname.
Recipients . . .

OFFICERS (O.B.E.)

1941	English. W.	Wardmaster Lieutenant
1944	Ball N. P.	Wardmaster Lieutenant
1945	Wilson E.	Commissioned Wardmaster
1946	Dickie R. E.	Wardmaster Lieutenant (Rtd).
1946	Peck S. H.	Wardmaster Lieutenant (Rtd).
1947	Britten W.	Warrant Wardmaster
1947	Rees P.	Warrant Wardmaster RNVR
1947	Birch H.	Wardmaster Lieutenant.
1970	Hamilton G. C.	Wardmaster Commander
1972	Vaughan D. J. L.	Wardmaster Commander.
1975	Clarkson T. R.	Commander (MS).
1978	Jackson A. A.	Commander (MS).
1982	MacKay A. C.	Commander (MS).

MEMBERS (M.B.E.)

1919	Budge H.	Warrant Wardmaster
–	Austin W.	Warrant Wardmaster
1937	Sabin P. R.	Commissioned Wardmaster
1938	Hoare, H. J.	Wardmaster Lieutenant.

1941	Jones A. E. CGM	Wardmaster Lieutenant.
1948	Blight W. G.	Wardmaster Lieutenant.
–	Carter I. G.	Wardmaster Lieutenant Commander.
1949	Hutley V. H.	Wardmaster Lieutenant Masseur to Prince of Wales in HMS *Renown* during the World Tour 1926
1951	May W. J. H.	Wardmaster Lieutenant.
1952	Levy J.	Wardmaster Lieutenant RAN
–	Tyler S. J.	Wardmaster Lieutenant.
1955	Mormemont W. M.	Wardmaster Lieutenant.
1958	Jenkins D. C.	Wardmaster Lieutenant.
1959	Masters A. E.	Wardmaster Lieutenant Commander.
1961	Jones W.	Wardmaster Lieutenant Commander.
1962	Lihou J. A.	Wardmaster Lieutenant Commander.
1963	Austin W. O. A.	Wardmaster Lieutenant Commander.
–	Banhard D.	Wardmaster Lieutenant.
1967	Montgomery T.	Wardmaster Lieutenant.
–	Saunders D. A.	Wardmaster Lieutenant.
–	Still C. A.	Commissioned Wardmaster.

THE BRITISH EMPIRE MEDAL (MILITARY DIVISION)

Follows DSM in order of Precedence.

1938	McClure D.	SBA for Meritorous service. CH.
1940	Jelley C. E.	SBPO.	CH.
1941	Croxford J. J.	SBCPO.	CH.
1941	Blandford I. G.	LSBA.	CH.
1941	Reed B. P.	SBCPO.	CH.
1941	Stanmore J. C.	SBPO.	PO.
1942	Thompson R. A.	SBA.	CH.
1942	Hains V. A.	Wardmaster Lieutenant. RAN.
1942	Cumber J. G.	SBCPO.	CH.
1942	Tonkin F.	SBCPO.	PO.
1942	Alexander J. H.	SBCPO.	PO.
1942	Bishop T. J.	SBCPO.	PO.
1942	Price S. R. T.	SBA.	DEV.
1942	Haden E. S. F.	SBA.	PO.
1943	McKenzie P. A.	SBPO SBR.
1943	Shelley D. E.	SBA	RAN.
1943	Pepitos E.	SBA	Free French Navy.
1943	Helme E.	SBA SBR.	DEV.
1943	Sloman L. M.	LSBA.	RAN.
1943	Stansmore J. C.	SBPO
1943	Guinigault J. A.	SBCPO	CH.
1943	Doidge W. H.	SBPO	DEV.
1943	Horn C. C.	SBPO.	DEV.

1943	Thompson E. H.	SBPO.	PO.
1943	Bailey J.	LSBA	DEV.
1943	Towler A. J.	SBCPO.	CH.
1943	Bishop T. J.	SBPO	PO.
1943	Powell F. M.	SBCPO.	DEV.
1943	McKenzie P. A.	SBPO	RAN
1943	Shelley D. E.	SBA	RAN.
1944	Gordon J. A.	SBCPO.	PO.
1945	Watkin W. M.	SBCPO.	PO.
1945	Edmondson D. E.	SBCPO.	PO.
1946	Baxendale W.	SBPO.	PO.
1946	Chambers J.	SBA.	PO.
1946	Cooke W. H.	SBCPO	DEV.
1946	Costagliola L.	SBPO	DEV.
1946	Dick D.	SBCPO.	DEV.
1946	Haddock H.	SBCPO.	CH.
1946	McCutcheon	SBA	CH.
1946	Price T.	SBCPO	CH.
1946	Stokes E. J.	SBCPO.	DEV.
1946	Taylor W.	SBCPO.	
1946	Watson R. A.	SBCPO.	CH.
1946	Arsenault R. P.	SBPO	RCNVR.
1946	Schnyper K.	SBPO.	RCNVR.
1946	Baker H. O.	LSBA.	PO.
1946	David J. A.	SBCPO.	CH.
1946	Forrest D.	SBCPO	DEV.
1946	Luckman S.	SBCPO.	CH.
1946	Lynch D.	SBCPO.	CH.
1946	O'Donnell J. S.	SBCPO.	DEV.
1946	Thomas L. R.	SBCPO.	DEV.
1946	Flynn P. J.	SBPO.	DEV.
1947	Banting J.	SBCPO.	PO.
1947	Randles W. J.	LSBA	PO.
1947	Gallagher F.	SBCPO.	PO.
1947	Thompson E. H.	SBCPO.	CH.
1952	Jones T.	SBCPO.	CH.
1952	Toulson F.	SBCPO.	CH.
1967	Rees C.	MT I.	
1972	McGinley R. J.	DSBA	RAN.
1972	Brown D. G.	CPOMA.	
1972	Reynolds J.	Head Naval Nurse.	
1972	Peterson D.	LMA	RNZN.
1972	James J.	POMA.	RM. Commando. Service in N. Ireland.

1972	Harrison E.	CPOMA.	RM. Commando. Service in N. Ireland.
1972	French.	CPOMA.	RM. Commando. Service in N. Ireland.
1972	Davies J.	CPOMA.	RM. Commando. Service in N. Ireland.
1972	Noble J.	CPOMA.	RM. Commando. Service in N. Ireland.
1973	Mason P. E.	CMT.(R).	DEV.
1973	Twigg D.	CMT.(R).	PO.
1973	Toll R. C.	CPOMA.	DEV.
1973	McKenzie J. C.	Wardmaster Commander.	
1973	Walker A. J.	Wardmaster Lieutenant.	
1973	Scoble C. J.	Commissioned Wardmaster.	
1977	Burton R.	CPOMA.	
1978	Nickson E.	CMT.(N).	
1978	Price.?	CMT.(N).	
1979	Lyons A.	CMT.	
1980	Knowles J. J.	A/POMA.	
1982	Rigby J.	POMA.(O).	
1982	Price D.	FCMA.	
1983	McKinlay S.	MTI.(I).	
1983	Fields M. R.	A/C.POMA.	
1983	Bogg R.	SBCPO (date appears incorrect before 1965).	
1983	Adams K.	FCMA.	
1983	Clements C.	SBCPO.	
1983	White M. A.	MTI.(N).	

The Royal Red Cross

Founded by Queen Victoria in a Royal Warrant dated 23rd April 1888 the award was given in two classes; First class known as Members and the Second class as Associates. The award was confined to ladies in the Nursing Services or to ladies who had given outstanding service in the care of the sick and wounded of the fighting Services.

On the 10th November 1915 an amendment was published restricting the Awards, RRC (the First Class) to 2 per cent of the Establishment and ARRC to 5 per cent of the Establishment. It is believed that these restrictions still stand.

A further amendment must have been made in the mid-seventies as it is now an award, albeit rare, to male members of the Nursing Staff of the Services viz:

1977	Wingett A. A.	CMT(N)	ARRC
1978	Hayward P. E.	FCMT(N)	ARRC
1979	Wellings P. R.	Lieutenant (MS)RN.	ARRC
1980	Hampton G.	FCMT(N)	ARRC

The Albert Medal

The announcement of this award came in a Royal Warrant dated 7 March 1866 viz:

Victoria by the Grace of God, of Great Britain and Ireland Queen, Defender of the Faith, Empress of India and of all our Dominions Overseas, Greetings.

A Warrant given under our Royal Sign Manual entitled a Warrant instituting a new decoration to be styled the Albert Medal.

In April 1867 the Medal was divided into two classes.

Albert Medal First Class was to be an oval medal on a blue ribband 1⅜ inches wide carrying four longitudinal stripes.

The second class was a similar medal in bronze on a blue ribband ⅝ inch wide and carrying two white longitudinal stripes.

Both were to be awarded for Gallantry in saving or attempting to save life at sea.

In April 1877 the award was extended to saving or attempting to save life on land. The only difference was that the ribband was crimson with the same arrangement of stripes for the first and second class.

In 1917 there was a change of names to Albert Medal in Gold and Albert Medal in Bronze.

In January 1969 it was decreed that all recipients would be entitled to an annuity of £100 a year.

The first Class in gold was abolished in favour of the George Cross, and in 1971 this was extended to include the second class in Bronze. At the same time, HM The Queen ordered that all living recipients of the Albert Medal should return them in exchange for the George Cross.

An indication of the esteem in which it was held by the general public was its unofficial name 'The Civilian V.C.'

Over the 103 years of its existence 69 Gold and 491 Bronze Albert Medals were issued. The youngest recipient was Anthony Fraser aged eight who saved an eleven year old girl companion from a cougar.

The medals bear an inscription on the reverse detailing the act of gallantry which led to the award.

The King has been graciously pleased to approve the award of the Albert Medal in Gold (Posthumous) to Arture Fanconi SBA, HMS *Odyssey* 1945.

On 28th June 1944 Fanconi was summoned to help men wounded

by mines at Quinville in Normandy. He at once ran almost half a mile and went through what later proved to be a field of anti-personnel mines to reach them.

He applied tourniquets and bandages, then with help carried two patients out of the drive which was the scene of the incident. This was a tiring and difficult task as it entailed hugging the wall all the way. Fanconi was on the more dangerous side throughout.

Whilst the reserve party was considering how best to help a third man who was lying some distance behind the minefield, another mine burst beneath the rubble on which they stood. This killed one helper and wounded Fanconi and another. Despite this Fanconi tried to collect his scattered medical kit and help his comrade. He had to crawl to do so and was in great pain.

In this attempt he exploded a further mine which blew off one of his feet. The explosion hurled him into the air and when he fell he set off a third mine which severed his other foot. A corporal made every effort to help him but his kit was of little use now and Fanconi could not be saved.

All who witnessed his selfless courage, his speed and his skill in giving aid to others, all the while exposing himself to immediate danger were inspired by his great example.

George William Beeching, SBA. HMS *Ibis* awarded the Albert Medal in 1943. Beeching was between decks when HMS *Ibis* was hit. The explosion caused damage and the ship took a list to starboard of about fifteen degrees. The emergency lighting partly failed and the messdecks were deep in oil. SBA Beeching showed great courage and presence of mind. He helped those who came forward with their wounds, among them was one man very badly burned about the face and hands. SBA Beeching took him to the sick bay and gave him morphia. When the ship began to heel over and it was apparent that she would capsize, he helped the man to the deck, gave him a lifebelt and got him into the water before abandoning ship himself. SBA Beeching was not seen again.

HMS *Ibis* was a Black Swan class escort sloop of 1250 tons armed with three twin mounts of 4 inch HA and one quadruple mounting of multiple 5 inch machine guns. She was lost on 10th November 1942, as a result of bomb damage inflicted by Italian aircraft. Ten of the Black Swan class sloops survived the war, two went to the Pakistan Navy, one to Egypt, one to West Germany renamed *Graf Spee* and HMS *Erne* became the RNVR Wessex HQ ship from 1952–1965.

William James Thorpe. SBA. HMS *Broke*. Awarded the Albert Medal in 1943. In a hazardous operation off the North African coast HMS *Broke* came under heavy fire. Many of her ships company were wounded. SBA Thorpe showed great courage in tending the wounded and getting them to places of greater safety. He himself was then mortally wounded but he spent his last strength caring for them until he could no longer stand. He died of his wounds.

HMS *Broke* was a Shakespeare class Flotilla leader of 1480 tons. Built in 1920 by Thornycroft, she was converted to a short range escort ship and rearmed with two 4.7 inch, one three inch HA and two quadruple 20mm pom pom guns.

She was lost while on detached service in the Mediterranean, having been damaged by shore batteries at Algiers on 8th November 1942 during the invasion of North Africa. She foundered the next day.

Thorpe was awarded the Albert Medal in Bronze (Posthumous).

The last Albert Medal awarded was to Fanconi.

The *Ibis* incident is the only one for which two Albert Medals in Gold were awarded.

In 103 years of its existence only 24 Albert Medals in Gold were awarded for gallantry at sea.

The Conspicuous Gallantry Medal

By an Order in Council dated 7th July 1874, a silver medal established for such Petty Officers and Seamen of the Royal Navy, and Non commissioned Officers and Privates of the Royal Marines, as may at any time distinguish themselves by acts of conspicuous gallantry in action with the enemy.

The conspicuous Gallantry Medal is a very rare Service award. Only 108 were given in the First World War, and 72 in the Second. There is only one recorded instance of a bar being awarded, this was to a Chief Petty Officer Blore in 1918.

T Gardener, SBS was one of the Senior ratings listed for the award of this medal. Officially the announcement was published thus . . .

'The Lords Commissioners of the Admiralty have awarded the Conspicuous Gallantry Medal to the undermentioned Petty Officers and men of the Royal Navy in connection with the recent operations in China.'

It is interesting to note that those awards were made direct by the Admiralty and not approved by the Crown Head.

There is no citation entry in the London Gazette, but the awards are listed in a small paragraph at the end of a routine list of naval promotions.

In the Naval medal rolls Gardener is listed as being awarded the Third China War Medal (10th June to 31st December 1900) with bar for relief of Pekin whilst serving in HMS *Barfleur*. Together with other Officers and Petty Officers, Gardener was presented with his medals on return to the UK by HM King Edward VII.

To Henry H. Hamblin Ch SBS HMS *Inflexible* in 1915 the CGM.

For services when HMS *Inflexible* was damaged by a mine on 18th March, Ch SBS Hamblin although overcome by fumes, assisted Surgeon Longford whilst *Inflexible* was proceeding to Tenedos.

The August despatch from Vice Admiral John De Robeck reported landings in Gallipoli on 25th, 26th April 1915, the following vessels being operational, HM Ships *Queen, London, Prince of Wales, Triumph, Majestic* (Battleships) the cruiser *Baccante*, 8 destroyers, 15 trawlers, the Seaplane carrier *Ark Royal* and the Balloon ship *Marice*.

To A. E. Jones SBS in 1916 the CGM.

Despatch from Admiral Sir John Jellicoe, GCB, GCVO, Commander in Chief Grand Fleet, reporting the action in the North Sea on 31st May 1916.

SBS Jones showed conspicuous gallantry in bringing hoses to bear on a cordite fire in the vicinity of the midship ammunition lobby when the supply parties had been driven away by fumes. He performed his duties in an exemplary manner in very trying circumstances. (Ship not mentioned).

Wardmaster Lieutenant A. E. Jones was the most decorated of all members of the Sick Berth Staff. He received the French Medaille Militaire in 1919, was recalled for service on the outbreak of the Second World War. He served at HMS *Royal Arthur* (ex Butlins Holiday Camp at Skegness, a new entry training establishment) where in 1941 he was awarded the MBE. In view of his white hair his nickname was Snowy. He thus finished his service as Wardmaster Lieutenant A. E. Jones, MBE, CGM, MM (France) – an example to us all.

In the same despatch a Posthumous VC was awarded to Boy 1st Class John Travers Cornwell, aged 16 in HMS *Chester*.

The George Medal

The George Medal and the George Cross were founded by King George Sixth in 1940.

It may be awarded to Officers and Men of the Royal Navy or of the Royal Marines for brave conduct on land or sea not in the presence of the enemy where the service is not so outstanding as to merit the award of the George Cross.

1972   McLoughlin   CPOMA.   45 Commando RM Belfast.

The Distinguished Service Medal

The institution of this award was published in the following manner.

'At the Court of Buckingham Palace on the 14th October 1914.

And whereas we are of the opinion that it would be desirable to establish a medal which could be awarded to the numerous instances where courage was shown in the war by Chief Petty Officers and men of your Majesty's Navy, and by Non Commissioned Officers and of your Majesty's Corps of Royal Marines, and all persons holding corresponding positions in your Majesty's Service afloat in cases where the award of the Conspicuous Gallantry Medal would be inappropriate.

We beg leave humbly to recommend that Your Majesty may be graciously pleased by your Order in Council to establish a medal to be called the Distinguished Service Medal, for such of the above classes of your Majesty's Navy as may at any time show themselves to be to the fore in action, and set an example of bravery and resource under fire, but without performing acts of such pre eminent bravery as would render them eligible for the Conspicuous Gallantry Medal.'

In 1916 dated bars to the medal were authorised for subsequent awards, but bars awarded previously were undated.

The ribbon consists of equal bands of dark blue, white and dark blue, with a narrow dark blue stripe down the central band of white.

Type of award The awards may be immediate, resulting from a mention in an operational despatch, or occasional, usually in the New Year or Birthday Honours' Lists.

In 1940 the DSM was made available to NCO's and men of the RAF serving at sea, and in later years it was extended to include NCO's and men serving afloat, for instance Maritime Royal Artillery, and to the Merchant Navy.

Numbers Awarded During the First World War over 5600 were awarded, these included fifty-three first bars and two second bars.

The Second World War resulted in the award of approximately 7700 of which 147 were first bars, three second bars, and a Petty Officer Kelly received the award on no less than four separate occasions.

Recipients of the Distinguished Service Medal include:

THE FIRST WORLD WAR

E. Walch SRA for operations around Antwerp from 3rd to 9th October 1914.

Despatch from Major Gen A. Paris CO RND 31st October 1914.

The Brigade (2200 all ranks) arrived in Antwerp during the night 3rd to 4th October. They occupied trenches facing Lierre relieving exhausted Belgian troops . . . . 5th to 6th October . . . . resulted in the evacuation of all the Belgian trenches, and the position of the Marine Brigade become untenable. Two Naval Brigades arrived during the night. Bombardment of the town forts and trenches began at midnight 7th to 8th October, water supply had been cut and soon 100 houses were burning. During the day it appeared that the Belgium Army could not hold forts any longer. About 5.30 pm on 8th I considered that if the Naval Division was to avoid disaster an immediate retirement was necessary. The retirement began at 7.30 pm and was carried out under very difficult conditions.

   28   killed
  167   wounded
2428   missing

To C. S. Hutchinson, SBA of HMS *Tiger* in connection with the action against the enemy in the North Sea in January 1915.

To T. E. Mullins SBA RAN 1915.

For his services in the action between HMAS *Sydney* and the German cruiser *Emden* on 9th November 1914.

Despatch from Captain C. T. Glossop RN reporting capture of *Emden*. Extract . . . Total casualties in *Sydney*: Killed 3, severely wounded 4. From *Emden* I had on board 30 officers and 53 men who were wounded, and of this number one officer and 3 men have since died of wounds . . . . and I cannot speak too highly of the Medical Staff and arrangements on subsequent trip (from North Keeling Island to Colombo), the ship being nothing but a hospital of the most painful description.

Emden left Vice Admiral Von Spee's East Asiatic Squadron on August 13th 1914 with collier *Markomannia*. In the following three months she sank or captured twenty merchant ships in a three month voyage through the Celebes and Flores Straits, Dutch East Indies, Sumatra, Malay Straits, Indian Ocean and Bay of Bengal. Her Captain Carl Von Muller decided to attack the British Cable and Wireless Station on Direction Island, one of the Cocos and Keeling Islands in the Southern Indian Ocean. A landing party was sent ashore on the morning of November 9th. They wrecked the wireless installation, blew up the WT mast and severed the undersea cables, but not before a signal had been transmitted by WT giving news of the arrival of *Emden*. This was picked up by HMAS *Sydney*, part of an escort to a large Anzac convoy. *Emden* sailed at 0940, sighted *Sydney* and opened fire.

She was outranged by *Sydney's* eight 6 inch guns against her own ten 4.1 inch. She was badly hit, guns and steering were damaged and unable to engage with guns or torpedoes Muller ran his ship aground on the reef surrounding North Keeling Island. She grounded at 1100. Muller was the last to leave his ship the next day, by which time the *Emden* had lost 141 dead and 65 wounded out of a ship's company of 323.

To George Stockham SBS Plymouth Battalion RMLI 1915 who was a member of a Naval Brigade which was used for special operations during the First World War. He was one of the men included in the general announcement viz:

'The following awards have been made to the Royal Naval Division . . . . During the night of May 9–10 in operations south of Achi Baba, Stockham worked splendidly under fire to recover wounded until he himself was severely wounded.' 5th August 1915.

Despatch from General Ian Mailton GHO Middle East Forces.

List of names deserving special mention . . . . Ply/SBS 491 Pte G Stockham.

It is interesting to note that in the Navy List of 1915 Stockham is listed as an SBA, yet in the London Gazette in both despatches he is recorded as a Private RMLI, both with the same Official number.

Undoubtedly he was a forerunner of the Commando Medical Assistant of today.

Royal Navy Division It was customary for many years to land Naval Brigades made up of Seaman and Marines from HM Ships. These Brigades were in action at the Crimea, the Indian Mutiny (as far inland as Lucknow) and in Colonial expeditions at Ashanti, East and West Coasts of Africa, Burma, China and South Africa.

The Royal Navy Division was originally formed from RNVR Officers and ratings in 1914 at Crystal Palace. It consisted of eight RN Battalions and four of the RMLI. Some were sent to Antwerp in October 1914. The main body or RND fought at Gallipoli and again in France and Belgium until 1918. They retained their Naval ranks and customs, including a daily rum issue, and were commanded throughout by RN officers. The famous New Zealander General Freyburg won his VC at Gallipoli in 1915 whilst serving as a junior Naval Officer in the RND. The Naval Battalions were named after famous Admirals, Drake, Hawke, Hood, Howe, Nelson, Anson, Benbow and Collingwood. The last two were disbanded after Gallipoli, to make up reinforcements for the other six before being drafted to France in May 1916. They wore distinctive brass badges on forage caps whilst in France. The Marine Battalions were named Chatham, Deal, Portsmouth and Plymouth and were joined in France by a Royal Marine Artillery and a machine gun Battalion with an Armoured Car Section.

To Thomas McNeill SRA 1916.

There is no additional information which accompanied his citation, although a previous entry on 21st January 1916 refers to the advance on Kut El Amara. It can be assumed that McNeill was serving in one of the River gunboats serving on the Tigris and Euphrates.

To Philip Charles Grillis. SRA 1916.

For his services in the Patrol Cruisers under the Command of Rear Admiral Sir Dudley R.S. De Chair KCB. MVO. during the period ending 31st December 1915.

To Albert Ernest Gregson Ch SBS 1916.

Harry Charles Pridmore 2SBS

Charles Purchase SBS

With reference to the despatch of Admiral Sir John Jellicoe first published in the London Gazette of Thursday July 6th 1916, the awards were made in connection with the recommendations of the Commander-in-Chief for services rendered by Petty Officers and men of the Grand Fleet in the action in the North Sea on 31st May–1st June 1916.

This referred to a very long despatch from Jellicoe dated HMS *Iron Duke* 24th June 1916 with details of the Fleet Action at Jutland.

On the afternoon of 31st May a clash occurred between the Battle Cruisers of Admirals Beatty and Hipper. The ensuing action continued throughout the night and involved the main British and German fleets. It was fought in haze and darkness, with visual communications made difficult by the haze of smoke, battleships engaging at a range of 20,000 yards and destroyers making torpedo attacks at 3000 yards and less. It was the encounter for which the Royal Navy had waited two years, and constituted what proved to be the greatest sea battle of all time, the like of which will never be seen again. During the action there were hits on five British battleships, six battlecruisers, eleven cruisers and fifteen destroyers. British losses were 3 battlecruisers, 4 cruisers and seven destroyers. The Germans High Sea Fleet sustained hits on twelve battleships, five battle cruisers, nine cruisers and eleven torpedo boats. Their losses amounted to one battleship, one battle cruiser, four cruisers and four torpedo boats.

The battle saw the advent of aerial reconnaissance. The Germans flew a Zeppelin above but it made no useful contribution to the engagement. Flight Lieutenant J Rutland (an ex-Lower Decker) with Assistant Paymaster G. S. Trewin as Observer took off in a float seaplane from HMS *Engadine*, flying under low cloud base at 900 ft and endeavoured to identify four enemy light cruisers. The first reports of the enemy were received in *Engadine* at 3.30 pm. The cruisers opened fire and a piece of shrapnel severed the petrol feed pipe and forced the plane down. This was the very first time that airborne reconnaissance had been carried out. Rutland received the DSO and became a Squadron Commander in the Battle Cruiser *Furious*, which with the forward turret removed carried out deck landing trials in Scapa Flow on 2nd August 1917. During a four months refit, her after turret was removed and the after landing deck which replaced it was connected by alley ways alongside the midships superstructure to the forward flying off deck. This arrangement was not a success; the superstructure amidships created air eddies and backwash, and the hot flue gases from the funnel caused additional complications. She was taken in hand after the Armistice and rebuilt on the lines of the Argue, the ex Italian liner Conte Rosso laid down in 1914, taken over by the Navy in 1916 and completed as an aircraft carrier in 1918. She had a clear stem to stern flight deck, but with a speed of only ten knots she was unable to keep up with the Fleet.

The following Sick Berth	A. E. Gregson	Ch SBS
personnel were awarded the	H. C. Pridmore	2nd SBS
Distinguished Service Medal.	C. Purchase	SBS
	C. R. Allwright	SBS

To Frederick Arthur Allen 2 SBS in recognition of his services in Destroyer Patrol Flotillas, Armed Boarding Steamers etc during the period which ended on 30th September 1916.

To Sampson Woodcock SBS. HMS *Challenge* 1917.
    Mentioned in despatches from C in C Cape of Good Hope for his services in coastal operations in HM Ships against German East Africa.

To Stanley Rothwell. Prob SBR in 1917.
and Arthur C. Abrahams 2nd SBS in 1918 DSM for actions which were not recorded.

To James MacDonald SBS 1918 for his action in the Heligoland Bight on the 17th November 1917.

To Ernest Thomas Young Acting Chief Sick Berth Steward in 1918 (no details given).

To Arthur Ernest Page SBS 1918 for his services in the operations against Zeebrugge and Ostend on the night of 22nd-23rd April 1918.
    The storming of the Mole at Zeebrugge was carried out by HM Ships *Vindictive, Iris II* and *Daffodil* (Two Liverpool ferry steamers). The blockships for the Bruges canal were the *Thetis, Intrepid* and *Iphigenia*. The *Sirius* and *Brilliant* were to be used as blockships at Ostend. The monitors *Erebus* and *Terror* were to bombard the vicinity of Zeebrugge and from Dunkirk the bombardment force for Ostend consisted of monitors Marshal Soult and five others. A fleet of tugs, minesweepers, picket boats together with 18 coastal Motor Boats and 33 Motor launches were in support with escorting French and British Destroyers, while the submarines C1 and C2 were to damage Zeebrugge viaduct.
    The storming force consisted of three Naval companies, and the 4th Battalion Royal Marines (The Immortal Fourth).
    The main Force sailed at 0453 on Monday 22nd April, monitors

bombarded Zeebrugge at 1120 pm. Ostend operators being timed simultaneously. The Storming party went ashore at midnight. An hour later *Vindictive* took on board survivors and pulled out as planned at 0015. C3 rammed the iron piers of the Viaduct, was abandoned at 0030, blown up and completely demolished the target. The *Thetis* went for the entrance to the Canal and, badly hit and with propellors fouled by net obstructions she sank close to the entrance. The two other Blockships penetrated the canal and were sunk by their crews across the canal. The Ostend Blockships failed to make their objective, partly due to a wind shift which exposed them to heavy fire, and partly because the entrance buoy had been moved some 2400 yards east. They both grounded and were sunk by their crews. From a total complement of 82 officers and 1698 men, some 176 were killed, 412 wounded and 49 were posted as 'missing'.

Many awards were made including 6 VC's, 21 DSO's, 29 DSC's, 16 CGM's and no less than 142 DSM's and 271 mentions in despatches among the latter being SBA Robinson and Senior Service Reserve Attendant Poynter. The last party of Zeebrugge veterans returned to the Mole for a Memorial service in 1982. In 1983 the Memorial at the end of the Mole was removed in order to make way for a car park. It has been relocated and rededicated, while the Burgomaster, the Town Council, British ex-Service Organisations and Belgium residents continue to pay annual homage on St Georges Day.

To Laurence Frederick Gibbons   2 SBS
Ernest George Seagers   2 SBS

The King was pleased to approve the awards for their services in Mesopotamia and the Persian Gulf. No mention was made of actions but they were probably for service in gunboats on the Rivers Tigris and Euphrates.

The following gunboats served on the Tigris, two occasionally being detached to Euphrates.

The ten new Insect class, HMS *Moth*, wearing the Flag of Captain Nunn SNO *Mesopotamia, Tarantula, Gnat* and 2 Fly Class. The Insect class were new constructions of 625 tons with a draught of only four feet and carried 2 six inch guns and a pom pom on a platform. After the war the Insect class were towed from UK to the China rivers by C class cruisers and sloops. The *Tarantula* served as SNO ship West River South China, and was joined by *Moth*. The *Gnat* and *Mantis* served on the Yangtse River, *Tarantula* escaped from Hong Kong to Ceylon in 1941 and served as an accommodation ship at Trincomalee, wearing the Flag of Commodore Highflyer. She was expended as a target on 1st May 1946, being ceremonially sunk by two C class destroyers who 'piped' her out of Trincomalee and manned ship as she passed.

The *Moth* was scuttled by her crew in Hong Kong Dockyard on 12th

December 1941. She was raised by the Japanese serving on the Yangtse as HIJMS *Suma*. There she was lost on 19th March 1945, having hit an aerial mine laid by a US Flying Fortress Bomber.

The *Gnat* arrived in the Mediterranean in 1940, was torpedoed and beached off the North African coast and used as an AA Platform. She was scrapped in 1945. The *Mantis* was involved in an incident on the Yangtse in 1926 when she was fired upon by Chinese artillery and sustained casualties. She was put up for disposal at Shanghai in January 1940, and was still awaiting disposal when the Japanese invaded in December 1941.

To John Layland   Prob SBR
Frank Edward James Morse   2 SBS
for services with the Royal Marine Artillery seige guns in Flanders in 1919.

To James Milner Cogwill   SBA
for services in 1918. Details of the circumstances were not given.

To Reginald George Young   SBA
for his services in the Caspian Sea during 1918–19.

THE SECOND WORLD WAR (DSM's continued)

1940 To Charles D. Pope SBCPO HMS *Exeter* in 1940
. . . . 'Who on returning from the fore part of the Sick Bay with bottles of morphine sulphate solution, was knocked flat and temporarily made unconscious by a shell bursting and badly perforating that end of the Sick Bay. The bottles were broken but when he recovered he went back through the smoke and fumes and not finding any more solution brought back with him morphine ampoules. Throughout the action he displayed great coolness, initiative and optimism despite floods in the Sick Bay. After the action his nursing and devotion to the wounded was exemplary.'

To Eric T. Dakin. SBA (Chatham) HMS *Exeter* in 1940
. . . .'Who had been in the ship only a week, having been lent from HMS *Ajax*, his first ship. His conduct throughout the action was exemplary. He carried out instructions perfectly, his first aid treatment was very good and his quiet, gentle manner gave great confidence to the wounded. His ability to take charge and keep order in difficulties was splendid.'

At dawn on December 13th 1939, smoke was seen on the horizon by HMS *Ajax*. HM Ships *Ajax*, *Achilles* and *Exeter* had been at dawn action stations, smoke was reported at 0609. Commodore Harwood signalled *Exeter* to close in and investigate. Captain Bell signalled 'I think it is a pocket battleship'. It was in fact the *Graf Spee*, which in five months at sea had traversed some tens of thousands of miles, and had sunk 50,000 tons of British merchant shipping. So started the battle of the River Plate. The British cruiser *Exeter* armed with six 8 inch guns firing a projectile weighing 250 lbs, the *Ajax* and *Achilles* each carrying eight 6 inch guns firing a projectile weighing 100 lbs, took on a pocket battleship armed with six 11 inch guns firing a projectile weighing 670 lbs. In addition the *Exeter* was outranged by two miles and the two six-inch cruisers by three miles. The *Graf Spee* had well armoured turrets as against the thinly protected hulls of the British cruisers.

Graf Spee opened fire at 0617 followed four minutes later by *Exeter*. The *Ajax* and *Achilles* were soon engaged by the secondary armament of the *Graf Spee's* 5.9 inch guns, almost an even match for the two light cruisers.

Just after 0730 the *Graf Spee* broke off the action, by which time the *Exeter* had all turrets out of action and was flooded forward. *Ajax* had X and Y turrets silenced, and *Achilles* had her Director Control destroyed. Shadowed by *Ajax* and *Achilles* the pocket battleship made for the River Plate, anchoring in Montevideo Roads at 0500 on December 14th. At 2054 on December 17th the *Graf Spee* was scuttled clear of the deep water channel. The Lords Commissioners of the Admiralty ordered the cruisers to sail for their ports after repairs. *Ajax* sailed into Devonport at dawn on 21st January 1940 although she was a Chatham manned ship and was followed in February by the *Exeter*.

On February 23rd 1940 led by the Royal Navy Marine Band Chatham Division, 760 Officers and men of *Ajax* and *Achilles* marched from Waterloo Station to Horse Guards Parade to be received by King George VI, the Duke of Kent, Winston Churchill, the First Lord of the Admiralty accompanied by the whole of his Admiralty Board, the Prime Minister and his Cabinet. After an inspection by His Majesty the parade marched to the Guildhall, there to be entertained to lunch by the Lord Mayor. It was very appropriate that the six Merchant Navy Captains who had been prisoners on *Graf Spee* were included in the parade, and that *Achilles* arrived at her home port in New Zealand on the same day.

The wrecked hull of the *Graf Spee* was sold to a South American salvage firm as scrap for £1000.

Exeter was subsequently sunk by Japanese naval vessels in the Java Seas: *Ajax* survived the war and was scrapped at Newport Mon, in November 1949.

The *Achilles* after serving in the New Zealand Navy until 1943 returned and finished the war in the Home Fleet with a brief period of service in 4th Cruiser squadron of the Pacific Fleet. In 1948 she was turned over to the Indian Navy and until two years ago served as INS

Delhi, when an unsuccessful attempt was made by Indian well wishers to preserve her.

To David Wright SBA HMS *Ashanti* in 1940

For his courage and resource in operations off the Norwegian coast. *Ashanti* was a Tribal class destroyer of 1870 tons built by Denny on the Clyde. She was armed with 4.7 inch guns in twin mountings and carried secondary A/A armament of four 2pdr and an eight barrelled multiple .5 machine guns. Her speed was 36 knots. She survived the war and was scrapped at Troon in April 1945 not far from the yard where she was built. It is interesting to note that the present ageing Tribal class frigates recently saved from the scrap yard have similar lines as the previous Tribal destroyers, with flared forecastles and raked funnels, the after one being shorter and giving an impression of speed. The Tribals, all built in 1937, were deployed in the 4th and 6th Destroyer Flotillas Home fleet at the beginning of WW2, and were considered to have the best lines of all ships in the Navy. Twelve of the 16 boats were lost in action between May 1940 and September 1942, the other four being scrapped in 1949.

To Stanley John Lively SBA in 1940

For his good services in the withdrawal of the Allied Armies from the beaches at Dunkirk.

To Harold Peacock P/SBR of HMS *Wyvern* in 1940

For his good services in operations off the Dutch, Belgian and French coasts.

To Ralph Edward Street LSBA of HMS *Highlander* in 1941

For his skill and determination during an action which resulted in the sinking of a German submarine.

Highlander was one of six destroyers built for the Brazilian Navy but taken over at the outbreak of war. They all served in the Western Approaches. The *Highlander* and *Harvester* sank the *U32* in the winter of 1940. *Highlander* survived the war and was scrapped at Rosyth in 1947.

To Alfred Harry Weeks SBCPO of HMS *Illustrious* in 1941

For his great courage and devotion to duty in the face of an enemy air attack. HMS *Illustrious* was the name of a class of aircraft carrier of 23,000 tons completed between 1939 and 1942. She was built at Vickers Armstrong, Barrow in 1939 and was followed by five others. She survived the war, and was scrapped at Faslane in November 1956. She served in the Mediterranean, Eastern and Pacific Fleets. She carried two flights of Swordfish and one flight of eight gunned Fulmar fighters.

Her Swordfish took part in the raid in Toranto. In the above action whilst escorting a Malta convoy in January 1941 she was attacked by Stukas of the Tenth Air Corps, which had arrived from bases on Sicily and Rhodes. She was the main target in the convoy and was hit by six 1000 lb bombs, her flight deck wrecked, her steering gear put out of action and damaged by several fires. Captain Boyd got her to Malta, where she was again repeatedly bombed, but was repaired and joined the Fleet at Alexandria on January 24th 1942.

To Henry Thomas Hicks SBCPO in 1941
For his outstanding zeal, patience and cheerfulness, and for never failing to set an example of wholehearted devotion to duty, without which the high traditions of the Royal Navy could not have been upheld.

To Frederick William John Hutter of HMS *Saltash* in 1942
For his outstanding zeal, patience and devotion to duty, without which the high traditions of the Royal Navy could have not been upheld.

To Oliver Clements SBCBS of HMS *Imperial* in 1942
For his courage resource, zeal and devotion to duty whilst serving with the Home Fleet in Norwegian waters and elsewhere in the Spring and Summer of 1940. The Imperial class destroyers were built between October 1936 and March 1937. They were of 1370 tons displacement, capable of 36 knots and armed with four 4.7 inch guns, two quadruple 0.5 inch AA guns and two banks of five 21 inch torpedo guns.

To William Ronald Aird SBPO of HMS *Perth*
Frank Clifford Harvison SBPO of HMS *Nubian*
and Edward John Denn SBPO of HMS *Orion*
'For their outstanding gallantry, fortitude and resolution during the battle of Crete.' In March 1941 there was fought an action which later became known as the battle of Matapan, *Orion* flew the flag of Vice Admiral D. H. Pridham Whippel. His command included HMS *Perth*. Both ships were armed with eight 6 inch guns and displaced over 7000 tons. HMS *Nubian*, a tribal class destroyer was one of the four ships of the 2nd and 10th Flotillas present. They engaged an Italian force of one battleship, four 8 inch cruisers and fourteen destroyers; three British battleships and the carrier *Formidable* was also involved. The Italian 8 inch cruisers, the *Pola*, *Zara* and *Fuime*, and two Italian destroyers were sunk during a brilliant night action. These three ships were also involved in the evacuation of troops from Crete. In five nights the Navy rescued nearly 51000 troops from Heraklion on the North coast and Spakhia in the south. In prolonged air attacks the *Orion* was severely hit and both forward turrets put out of action, with numerous casualties among the crew and soldiers who were packed on the deck.

Orion survived the war and was scrapped at Troon in 1949. *Perth* was transferred to the Far East and was sunk by Japanese surface craft in the Sunda Straits on March 1st 1942. *Nubian* continued to serve with the Fleet in Home and Mediterranean waters, and was one of the four survivors of the Tribals which finished the war in the Far East as the 14th Flotilla. She was scrapped at Briton Ferry in June 1959.

To William Robert Stanmore SBA in 1942
'For Distinguished service in HM Ships taking convoys to Murmansk, through the dangers of ice and heavy seas, in the face of relentless attacks by enemy U boats, aircraft and surface forces.'

To Albert Edward Rogers SBA in 1942
'For his gallantry, skill and seamanship in HM Ships in a brilliant action against strong enemy forces which were driven off and severely damaged; this action resulted in the safe passage of an important convoy.'

To Matthew Adolphus Howden SBPO RAN of HMAS *Hobart* in 1942
'For his bravery and endurance when HMAS *Hobart* was taking convoys across the China Seas.'
Hobart was a Leander class cruiser built by Beardmore in 1934. Together with her two sister ships *Sydney* and *Perth* she was built for and commissioned in the Australian Navy. *Hobart* served also in the Red Sea, the East Indies and in Australian waters. She was eventually scrapped in Japan in March 1962.

To Charles Ephraim Buddin SBPO of HMS *Cairo* in 1942
'For his bravery and resolution in HM Ships whilst escorting an important convoy.'
During June 14th *Cairo* was in action with strong enemy air forces, and on June 15th was engaged with a superior enemy force. On June 14th Buddin showed skill and devotion to duty in tending the wounded and on June 15th, when severely wounded in the surface action, showed unselfishness in requesting the Medical Officer to leave him until all the wounded had been seen. *Cairo* was a Capetown class cruiser launched eight days after the Armistice which ended the first World War. She was a light cruiser of 4290 tons displacement. Her armament of five 6 inch and two 8 inch AA guns was replaced by eight 4 inch AA and four 2pdr AA guns, and she served in the Home and Mediterranean Fleets as an AA cruiser. Three Ceres class and four Capetown class were also converted. *Cairo* was torpedoed and sunk by an Italian submarine, the *Axum*, north of Bizerta on 12th August 1942.
Report from Commodore of Convoy. Commander J. P. W. Pilditch RN(Rtd) At dawn on 15th June an enemy surface force was sighted on

port bow about ten miles distant. In the dim light I estimated the force to consist of two large cruisers, presumably 8 inch, two smaller 6 inch cruisers and four or more larger all with a speed of about 37 knots. *Cairo* immediately took on all the destroyers and told me to take charge of the Convoy. The Italians opened fire at extreme range and salvoes immediately fell close to the Convoy.

Footnote. Prior to the 1939–45 war Buddin gained the Naval General Service Medal (Clasp Palestine 1936–39). It is interesting to note that together with many of his pensioner contemporaries who were kept on for the duration of the war, Petty Officer Buddin received the extra sum of 2d per diem, which is less than 1p daily in current cash: what was then termed 'retained' pay.

Convoy hero now an MBE After losing a leg and gaining the DSM in the Malta convoy action Mr C. Buddin was invalided out of the Royal Navy in 1944. A regular service man, he joined the RN in 1920 and would normally have been discharged in 1942. Soon after being invalided from the Navy, he moved to Portsmouth and became Assistant Secretary to the Local Committee of the Royal Naval Benevolent Trust taking up his appointment five years later. A founder member of the Board of Management of the BLESMA Home in Southsea, Mr Buddin by virtue of his position was on a number of voluntary welfare committees in Portsmouth. He died in 1971.

To Erza White Foden SBA

  Henry William Kelsey SBA in 1942

'For their gallantry and skill in the combined attack on Dieppe. On 19th August a major raid on Dieppe took place. The 2nd Canadian Division (General Roberts) with Commando units and some French and US troops made up a strength of 6000 men. The raid was designed to improve battle experience and to gain information about German defence methods which might be useful in the future. Few of the targets marked for destruction were reached, and only a small proportion of the landing force could be taken off. Losses totalled 3600 men, 106 aircraft, 30 tanks, 1 destroyer and 33 landing craft. German losses were 600 men and 30 planes. Militarily it was a disaster, but lessons learned on effective preliminary bombardment, and the use of specialised personnel, equipment and craft needed for beach landings, were subsequently put to very good use in the Normandy landings.

To Percy Hackett SBA in 1942

'For his bravery and resolution in HM Ships, HM Aircraft Carriers, merchantmen and oilers when an important convoy was fought through to Malta in the face of relentless attacks by day and by night by enemy submarines aircraft and surface forces.'

To Ronald Gordon James Turner SBA in 1942
'For his gallantry leadership and devotion to duty in HM Ships escorting on important convoy to Russia in the face of relentless attacks by enemy aircraft and submarines.'

To Daniel Albert Lock SBA in 1942
'For his gallantry, leadership and devotion to duty in HM Ships *Sikh, Zulu* and other ships in the raid on Tobruk in September 1942.'

To Harold Rodney Plant Sick Berth Assistant
'For his gallantry and outstanding services in the face of the enemy, and for zeal patience and cheerfulness in dangerous waters, and for setting an example of wholehearted devotion without which the high tradition of the Royal Navy could not have been upheld.'

To Norman Claude Morgan SBA of HMS *Thraser* in 1943
'For his gallantry, skill and devotion to duty in the face of persistent air attack when his ship was damaged.'
Two DSM were awarded, one to a Sick Berth Assistant and one to Ldg Cook. *Thraser* was a T class submarine built by Cammell Laird in November 1940. In January 1942 8 T Class were deployed to 1st Flotilla based on Alexander, 3 in the 3rd Flotilla based on the Clyde, 1 in the 6th Flotilla at Blyth and 2 in the Eastern Fleet. Sick Berth Staff were not part of the normal complement of submarine during the Second World War.

To Thomas Hanley SBA of HMS *Broke* in 1943
'For bravery in Northern waters.'
HMS *Broke* was a Shakespeare class Flotilla leader of 1480 tons built in 1920 and converted for escort duties at the outbreak of the war. Her armament consisted of two 4.7 inch, four 20mm AA guns and six 21 inch torpedo tubes. She served in the Home fleet and Rosyth Escort force during the war and was detached for the invasion of North Africa, where on 8.11.42 she was damaged by shore batteries at Algiers and foundered the next day.

To Gilbert Ferguson Gallagher SBA in 1943 whilst serving in HMS *Queen Emma*.
'For fortitude and great devotion to duty and service to the wounded when his ship was attacked from the air. Only one award to this ship was made during the assault on the Padrina Penisula.'

To Edwin Joseph Burton SBA in 1944
'For his gallantry, leadership and undaunted devotion to duty under

14   RNH Haslar. The new look

15   RNH Plymouth 1975

16 RN Hospital Bighi, Malta

17 'A' block, RN Hospital Chatham *c*1960

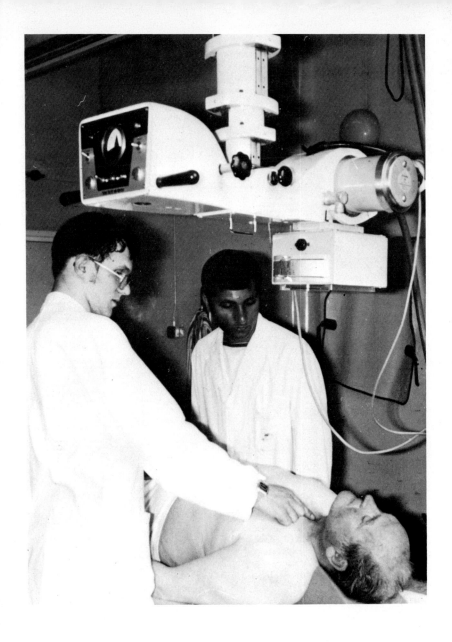

18   A Medical Technician instructs a student Radiographer on positioning a patient for radiographic examination of the cervical spine

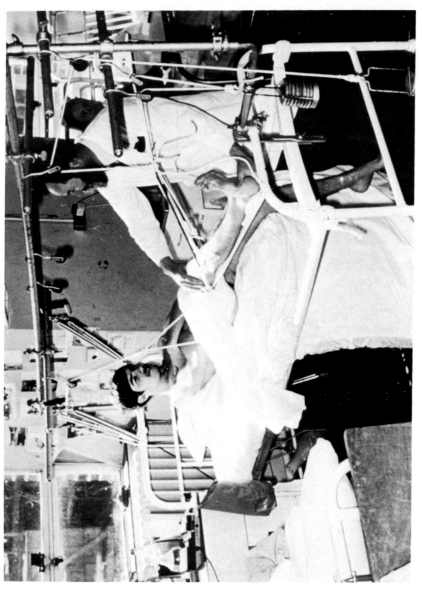

19 A Medical Technician (Physiotherapist) treats a patient in RN Hospital Haslar

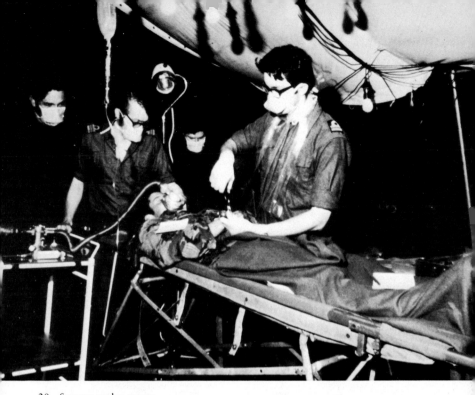

20 Surgery under canvas

21 RM medical team in snow

22 A ship-born casualty handling exercise demonstrating one role of the Neil Robertson stretcher

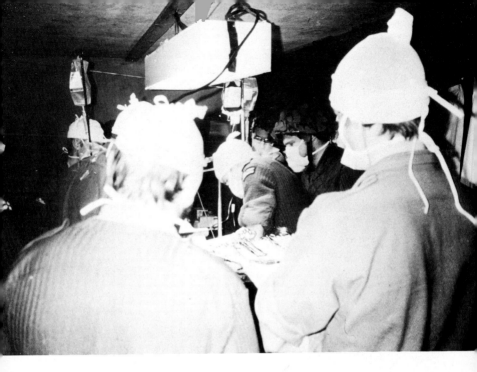

23   The medical team operating on casualties

24   Unloading casualties

25 Burns victims from *Sir Tristram* and *Sir Galahad* receiving treatment

heavy and continuous fire from the enemy during landings on the Italian mainland.'

To Robert Wainwright SBA in 1944

'For undaunted courage, determination and endurance whilst serving in RN Ships during many sweeps against enemy shipping in the Aegean whilst under constant attack from the air and in maintaining supplies to the Islands of Kos and Leros until they fell to superior enemy forces.'

To Emlyn Jones SBA in 1944

'For his gallantry, skill and undaunted devotion to duty during the initial landing of Allied Forces on the coast of Normandy.'

To Michael Fay SBA of Liverpool in 1944

'For his distinguished services in operations carried out in the face of determined opposition from the enemy, which led to the capture of the Island of Elba.'

1944

To	Leslie Charles Dewey	SBPO	DSM	
	John Rutter	LSBA	(Southampton)	DSM
	Henry Robert Hutchinson	SBA	(Gateshead)	DSM
	James Narcy	SBA	DSM	
	Stanley George Willmott	SBA	(North Finchley)	DSM
	Thomas Elwin Wilson	SBA	DSM	

'For their gallantry, skill and determination and undaunted devotion to duty during the landings of Allied Forces on the coast of Normandy.'

1945

To	Henry James Gibson	SBCPO (Chatham) HMS *Mauritius*	DSM
	James Lawrence	SBCPO (Saltash) HMS *Victorious*	DSM

The King was graciously pleased to approve the awards of the Distinguished Service Medal for gallantry and outstanding service in the face of the enemy, for their zeal, patience, and cheerfulness in dangerous waters, and for setting an example of whole hearted devotion to duty without which the high traditions of the Royal Navy could not have been upheld.

To John Ferguson, LSBA of Stockton on Tees

'For his gallantry and devotion to duty whilst serving in the care of the wounded on the assault beach at Walcheren.'

To Robert Victor Goodwin   SBCPO RAN and
    Francis Patrick Dargan   SBPO RAN in 1945

'For their gallantry, skill and devotion to duty whilst serving in HM Australian ships in the successful operations on the Lingayen Gulf, Luzon Island.'

To Alexander Mordie Smith SBA of Preston Pans, Lothian in 1945
    For gallantry and devotion to duty whilst serving in HMS *Valorous* and HMS *Verdum* in seeking out U Boats and beating off a series of attacks on a convoy.
    Valorous and *Verdum* were old destroyers built during the First World War. They were converted to Escort destroyers and rearmed with four, 4 inch HA and A/S weapons. They served in the Western approaches and on the East coast (E.Boat Alley), escorting coastal convoys from Methil to South Coast ports. Both survived the war and were scrapped in the mid forties.

To Herbert John Pullin SBPO (Ty) of Bristol
and Leslie George Spencer LSBA in 1945
    'For their gallantry in the face of the enemy, and their cheerfulness in dangerous waters and for setting an example of whole hearted devotion to duty, upholding the high traditions of the Royal Navy.'

To Roland Hubert Roagers SBA
and Anathamar Bose RIN in 1945
    'For their courage, tenacity, and devotion to duty whilst serving in HM Ships and HM Indian ships and light Coastal forces in operations lasting four months under rapidly changing conditions and with difficult lines of communication on the Arakan coast.'

'To Thomas Gavin Rutherford SBCPO in 1945
    For his outstanding courage and devotion to duty when HMS *Bedouin* was sunk in defence of a convoy to Malta.'
    HMS *Bedouin*, a Tribal class destroyer, built by Denny and launched in November 1937, was torpedoed by Italian aircraft on 15th June after having been damaged by gunfire inflicted by the Italian cruiser *Savioa*. Rutherford spend the rest of the war in an Italian POW Camp and was subsequently promoted Warrant Wardmaster before retiring.

To Alan Frederick Cole SBA RAN in 1945
    'For his courage, endurance and skill whilst serving in HM Australian Ships on escort duties for more than three years under hazardous and trying conditions between the Australian coast and the Philipine Islands.'

To Samuel Westwood SBCPO   DSM
    Thomas Raby LSBA   DSM
and Eric Barber SBA   DSM
    'For their distinguished service in 1945 during the War in Europe'.

To James Cunningham SBPO RAN
    'For his gallantry and resolution whilst serving in HMAS *Perth*, lost by enemy action in the Far East on March 1st 1945'.

To Harry Burton SBCPO in 1946 DSM
    'For his distinguished service during the war in the Far East.'

Queens Gallantry Medal
The Queens Gallantry Medal was awarded to Petty Officer Medical Assistant G. A. Meager for his gallant action on board HMS *Sheffield* on 4th May 1982 during the Falkland's campaign. A personal account of his action is given in Chapter 7.

Mentioned in Despatches

These ratings were singled out by name and mentioned in despatches to the Admiralty by CinC's, Flag Officers and Officers in operational commands as being worthy of special mention.

    No emblem was worn until after the conclusion of World War 1. In 1920 King George the Fifth approved the wearing of Bronze oak leaves on the ribbon of the Victory Medal. This signified one or more mentions.

    In 1943 King George the Sixth approved the wearing of a silver oak leaf for mentions in World War 2. It was worn on the jacket until the issue of the 1939–45 War Medal, when it was transferred to that ribbon.

    The emblem continues to be worn on the jacket for mentions where no campaign medal has been issued.

1900	Philips W. J.	SBS	Landed with the Naval Brigade from HMS *Doris*. In the course of one year, the field guns were manhandled across over 800 miles of open country, and were in action many times.
1914	Trolley G.	SBS	HMS *Arethusa* 28th August Battle of Heligoland Bight.
1915	Young W. H.	SBS	Commended
1916	Allwright C. R.	SBS	Battle of Jutland.
1919	Wright G. W.	SBS	Battle of Jutland.
1916	Beal J. G.	CH SBS	Battle of Jutland.
1916	Lloyd V.	SBS	Battle of Jutland.

1916 Camm. A. G.	CH. SBS	Battle of Jutland.
1916 Gardner W.	SBS	Battle of Jutland.
1916 Herbert L. G.	SBS	Battle of Jutland.
1916 Mortimer S. R.	SBA	Battle of Jutland.
1916 Neal J. A.	Ch SBS	Battle of Jutland.
1916 Pearce W. H.	SBS	Battle of Jutland.
1917 Grieve G. J.	SBA	
1917 Sabin L. I. P.	SBS	
1917 Woodcock S.	SBS	
1918 Cole E.	SBA	
1918 Collins W. J.	SBS	
1918 Haslam R.	Wardmaster	
1918 Mobbs E. J. B.	SBS	
1918 Bamberg J.	SBA	
1918 Hardwick P.	SBA	
1918 Hill H.	Senior Reserve Attendant.	
1918 Poynter E. G.	Senior Reserve Attendant.	
1918 Robinson A.	SBA	
1918 Crofts C. E.	SBS	
1918 Purdue H. R.	SBS	
1918 Watterson R. A.	SBA	
1919 Beale F. C.	SBS	
1919 Hadder W.	ChSBS	
1919 Downing A.	SBS	
1919 Barks A. G.	SBS	
1919 Trow H. J.	Senior Reserve Attendant.	
1919 Garvan A. C.	ChSBS	
1919 Gurney A. T.	Reserve Wardmaster	
1919 Hart C. W.	2SBS	
1919 Hickey A. G.	ChSBS	
1919 Jenkinson P. G.	ChSBS	
1919 LeBreton W. A. G.	SBA	
1919 McLoughlin R. G.	2SBS	
1919 Mantell E. G.	ChSBS	
1919 Padwick R. L.	SBS	
1919 Sabin R. R.	SBS	
1919 Tyler A. H.	2SBS	
1919 White G. E.	SBS	
1919 Wood C.	ChSBS	
1940 Hawkins H. W.	SBPO	
1940 Groves W. H.	SBPO	
1940 Lockwood R. H.	SBPO	
1940 Wright G. R.	SBPO	
1940 Martin N. C.	LSBA	
1940 Gibson E. T.	SBA	

1940	Kellar A.	SBA	SBR	
1940	Tomlinson J. T.	SBA	SBR	
1940	Welch E.	SBA	SBR	
1940	Yeoman J.	SBA	SBR	
1940	Sharp J. L.	SBA	SBR	CH
1940	Watson H.	SBA	SBR	DEV
1940	Smith H.	SBA	CH .	
1940	Shellum F.	PSBA	CH	
1940	Hicks G. T. H.	SBCPO	DEV	
1941	Dinnage H. E.	SBCPO	HMS *Furious*	
1941	Horsham T. H.	SBPO	HMS *Furious*	
1941	Townsend W. G.	SBPO	HMHS *Maine*	
1941	Burridge W. J.	SBPO	HMS *Terror*	
1941	Cowley C. J.	SBA RAN	HMS *Waterhen*	
1941	Whittington R. W.	SBA	HMS *Aurora*	PO
1941	Steggles R. G.	SBA	HMS *Kelvin*	CH
1941	Greisedale J. H.	LSBA SBR	HMS *Javelin*	CH
1941	Reyes W. A.	LSBA	(Posthumous)	CH
1941	Bradshaw T.	SBA	DEV	
1941	Beyon A. W. H.	SBA	DEV	
1941	Gime W.	SBPO SBR	PO	
1941	Whittington D. L.	SBA	HMS *Aurora*	PO
1941	Harper W. E.	SBA	PO	
1941	Denn E. J.	LSBA	HMS *Orion*	CH
1941	Lipham K.	SBA RAN	HMAS *Perth*	RAN
1941	Porter A. L.	LSBA	HMS *Grimsby*	CH
1942	Pearson G. E.	SBPO	CH	
1942	Goodwin L. E.	SBA	CH	
1942	Shelley A. J.	SBA	DEV	
1942	Whitworth A.	SBA	DEV	
1942	Manning F. O.	SBPO	CH	
1942	Spawdon E. G.	SBA	DEV	
1942	Geery P.	SBA	PO	
1942	Cleare G. H.	SBA	CH	
1942	Marden C. E.	LSBA	RAN	RAN
1942	Stevens M. E.	LSBA	CH	
1942	Bridgewater W.	SBA	CH	
1942	Batterton J.	SBA	DEV	
1942	Main F.	SBA	PO	
1942	Aulton F.	SBA	SBR	PO
1942	Betham R.	SBA	SBR	DEV
1942	Halls A. C.	SBPO	SBR	CH
1942	Leckie N.	SBA	RCNVR	RCN
1942	Preston C.	SBPO	SBR	PO
1943	Broughton A. E.	SBA	HMS *Marne*	PO

1943	Davis A. R.	SBA	SBR	DEV
1943	McMillan W. E.	LSBA SBR	HMS *Pelican*	CH
1943	Duncan J. T. M.	SBPO	DEV	
1943	Thorne W.	SBA	Loss of HMS *Dorsetshire*	SNAF
1943	Draycott C. G.	LSBA	CH	
1943	Stafford A. A.	SBA	HMS *Whitley Bay*	CH
1943	Bailey J.	SBA	For good services to survivors in the water when HMS *Egret* was lost	PO
1943	Piggott J.	LSBA SBR	CH	
1943	Johnson T. H.	SBA		PO
1943	Mackney E. G.	SBPO	PO	
1943	Preston C.	SBPO	SBR	DEV
1943	Dench H. W.	SBCPO	CH	
1943	Murray J.	SBCPO	PO	
1943	Treadwell E. W.	SBCPO	DEV	
1943	Game J. F.	LSBA(TY)	SBR	CH
1943	Draycott C. G.	LSBA	CH	
1943	Sloman L. M.	LSBA	RAN	RAN
1943	Bateman C. E.	SBA	RCNVR	RCN
1944	Stokes R. E.	SBCPO	RM Crete	DEV
1944	Derrick J.	SBA	CH	
1944	Jamieson R. M.	SBA	HMS *Cumberland*	CH
1944	Bowhay G.	SBA	DEV	
1944	Lucas J.	LSBA	DEV	
1944	Whittington F. C. A.	SBA	DEV	
1944	Main H.	SBCPO	PO	
1944	Craven N.	SBA	RNZN	RNZN
1944	Marshall R.	SBCPO	PO	
1944	Humphries R. C.	SBA	SBR	DEV
1944	Cranshaw N. S.	SBA	PO	
1944	Moorby V.	SBA	PO	
1944	Ingleson H.	SBA	PO	
1944	Hill J.	SBPO	SBR	CH
1944	Spencer J.	SBA	SBR	PO
1944	Wintrop L. J.	SBA	PO	
1944	Beard J.	SBA	PO	
1944	Cavill A. L.	LSBA	PO	
1944	Knox F.	SBPO	Normandy Landings	DEV
1944	Stansmore J. C.	SBCPO	Normandy Landings	PO
1944	Potter L. I.	SBA	RCN	RCN
1944	Main H. W.	SBCPO	Normandy Landings	PO
1945	Banks W.	SBA	Normandy Landings	CH

1945	Drummond R. A.	SBA	Walcheren Landings	CH
1945	Jenkins N. G.	SBA	DEV	
1945	Smalley F.	SBA	DEV	
1945	Gallagher J.	SBA	Normandy Landings	DEV
1945	Ridgeway H.	SBA	Normandy Landings	PO
1945	Mosher S. B.	SBA RCN	RCN	
1945	Dargon F. P.	SBPO RAN	HMAS *Australia*	RAN
1945	Gerret C. V.	SBPO RAN	HMAS *Australia*	RAN
1945	Newton E. C. R.	SBA RAN	HMAS *Australia*	RAN
1945	Haskell C. R.	SBA RAN	HMAS *Australia*	RAN
1945	Davies R. A.	LSBA	HMS *Rutherford*	DEV
1945	Patey E. G.	SBA	Attack by E. Boats	CH
1945	Doodson W.	SBA	Relief of Antwerp	DEV
1945	Gibson J.	SBPO	HMS *Dandelion*	CH
1945	Danson R.	SBA	HMS *Lookout*	DEV
1945	Shepherd L.	SBA	Relief of Greece	DEV
1945	Brown L.	SBA	Russian convoy action	DEV
1945	Hallam E.	SBA	Torpedoed Merchant ship rescue	DEV
1945	Mayes H. R.	SBPO	Assault on Borneo	
1945	Farquhar A. A.	SBPO RAN	HMS *Westralia*	RAN
1945	Sutton J. H.	SBCPO	HMS *Dorsetshire*	PO
1945	Bryant G. S.	SBA	HMS *Dorsetshire*	DEV
1945	Grant D. E.	SBPO	Operations off Selang	PO
1945	Brewer W.	SBPO	Capture of Okinawa with US	PO
1945	Hubble L.	SBPO	Capture of Okinawa with US	PO
1946	Anthony J. F.	SBCPO	PO	
1946	Burton H.	SBCPO	CH	
1946	Heath D. C.	SBCPO	CH	
1946	Spelman E. P.	SBCPO	CH	
1946	White A. G.	SBCPO	DEV	
1946	Martin D. M.	SBA RCNVR	RCN	
1946	Mitchell A.	SBA RAN	RAN	
1946	Pryce M.	Warrant Wardmaster. Service in Far East		
1946	Lee S.	SBCPO	Service in Far East	DEV
1946	Grass F.	SBCPO	Service in far East	CH
1946	Webb R. J.	SBCPO	Service in Far East	PO
1946	Davies A. C.	SBPO	Service in Far East	PO
1946	Piggott J.	SBPO SBR	Service in Far East	CH
1946	Danby W.	SBA	Service in Far East	CH
1946	McCready T.	SBPO	Good services whilst POW in far East	DEV

1946	McGreen T.	SBPO	Good services whilst POW in Far East	DEV
1946	Shipsides K.	LSBA	Good services whilst POW in Far East	DEV
1946	Hasting G. W.	SBPO	Good services whilst POW in Far East	CH
1946	Gould A.	SBCPO	Good services whilst POW in Far East	DEV
1946	Hughes J. E.	LSBA	Good services whilst POW in Far East	POWPO
1952	Baird. ?.	SBA	41 RM Commando Chosin Reservoir. Korea	
1964	Wade T.	LSBA	RM Commando Aden 1964	
1982	Youngman P.	LMA	45 RM Commando, Falklands	
1982	Black G.	ALMA	40 RM Commando, Falklands	
1982	Nicely M.	MA	45 RM Commando, Falklands	

Commendations

Queens Commendation for valuable services in the air

1979 LMA STEELE The commendation was made for the part he played when a Sea King from RNAS *Culdrose* rescued eight fishermen from the trawler *Ben Asdale* which foundered on rocks off Maenporth in heavy seas on New Years Eve 1978. Lieutenant Commander Norman and Lieutenant Hogg, the pilot and observer were awarded the Air Force Cross.

Queens Commendation for Brave Conduct

was made to CPOMA Harrison in 1958 whilst serving on a survey ship

The Meritorious Service Medal

The MSM which is not considered to be in the Honours and Awards category was first listed as an award to the Royal Navy in the Navy List of 1919.

It was discontinued in 1928, and re-instituted in December 1977.

1919	Howe A. D. G.	Reserve Wardmaster
1919	Newns J. E.	Reserve Wardmaster
1919	Kelleway H. W.	SBS
1919	Capp G. F.	SBS
1919	Hall F. T.	SBS
1919	Whitcombe A. H.	SBS
1919	Freckleton L. G.	SBS
1919	Yaxley B. R.	SBS
1919	Amey H.	SBS
1919	Francis R.	ChSBS
1919	Crofts C. E.	SBS
1919	Kellaway J. R.	SBS
1919	Seton C. C. C.	SBA
1919	Webber V. A. W.	SBA
1919	Brown H. J.	ChSBS
1919	Burgess C. B.	SBS
1919	Fitzgerald R. C.	ChSBS
1919	Fleming A. E.	Senior Reserve Attendant SBR
1919	Glover W. J. H.	ChSBS
1919	Gregory J. J.	SBS
1919	Hicks C. W.	SBS
1919	Hoddle H. G.	SBS
1919	Lamb S. H.	Reserve Wardmaster
1919	Maynard H. E.	Senior Reserve Attendant
1919	O'Leary T. J.	ChSBS
1919	Olver W. G.	SBS
1919	Turnbull E. J.	SBS
1919	Payne W. H.	ChSBS
1919	Speak W. E.	Senior Reserve Attendant
1919	Underhill E. J.	SBS
1919	Cross R.	SBA
1919	Burrows W. J.	SBS
1919	Hill F. C.	ChSBS
1920	Crane S.	SBS
1920	Bellairs A.	ChSBS
1920	Harris G. S.	ChSBS
1923	Richards A. G.	SBPO (acting) Awarded for services at
1923	Eyles. C. V.	LSBA RNSQ Yokohama which
1923	Bilton. W.	SBA was destroyed by fire and
		earthquake in September
		1923

W. Bilton retired as a Warrant Wardmaster, was recalled at the outbreak of the Second World War, and served in

HMHS *Oxfordshire* throughout the North African, Sicilian and Italian campaigns. A mild kindly man, always known as 'Rob' Wilton who as many will remember was a one time comedian.

Reintroduced after a gap of nearly 50 years, a list of 77 awards back-dated to 1977 and 1978 was promulgated in 1979. These included the following personnel . . . .

1977	Fearnley D. G.	FCMA	Devonport
1978	Dongworth	FCMA	Devonport
1978	Saunders	FCMT	Devonport
1980	Burton K. C.	CPOMA	Devonport
1983	Lyons A.	CMT	Devonport

Medals of the Humane Society

The Royal Humane Society was set up as long ago as 1714, and awards of silver and bronze which recognised acts of courage involving the rescue of humans or animals.

| 1906 | Finch C. S. | SBS | Bronze Medal |
| 1921 | Hubbard W. H. | SBA | Bronze Medal |

The circumstances leading to these awards are not known

Foreign Decorations and Awards

A large number of foreign awards were made by the Allies to the British Services during and immediately after the First World War. These were gazetted and carried permission for them to be worn on uniforms. The majority were Orders granted to Officers. Some however were received by ratings and among them were:

Croix de Guerre (France)
| Pert C. H. | ChSBS | 1919 |

Roumanian Distinguished Conduct Medal, 2nd Class
| Gradwell J. | SBA | 1919 |

Medaille Militaire (France)
| Hamblin H. H. | ChSBS | 1919 (also held CGM) |
| Jones A. E. | SBS | 1919 (also held CGM) |

Gold Medal for Zealous Service (Serbia)
| Collins | SBA | 1919 |

Crix de Cuerre (Belgium)
| Harris C. T. | SBS | 1919 |

The Sick Berth Petty Officer's Efficiency Medal

On 21st May 1919 a letter received by the Secretary to the Admiralty was circulated to the Medical Director General for remarks:-

Primrose Club
Park Place
St James S.W.
2 April 1919

The Secretary of Admiralty
Dear Sir,

Will you kindly inform me whether the Lords Commissioners of the Admiralty would be willing to institute an annual medal to be presented to the member of the Sick Berth Staff of his Majesty's Navy who has shown the greatest zeal and efficiency during the previous year.

If in the affirmative I would deem it a privilege to subscribe one hundred pounds for this purpose, the gift to be anonymous.

I had intended to leave this amount by will but perhaps I may be permitted to anticipate, trusting that this year will see the signing of the Peace,

I am Dear Sir,
Your obedient Servant,
F . . . . W . . . . C . . . .
Surgeon Rtd RN

A file was duly initiated and circulated to the Second Sea Lord, the Fourth Sea Lord, Medical Director General, N Branch, and their Principal Secretaries. The first annotation, signed N. Skinner 14.4.19 states:

'The procedure for the award of such a medal or prize might follow the award of the Llewelyn Prize recently instituted. Papers attached.' (This was a cash prize to be awarded to selected Gunnery ratings). The Medical Director General Surgeon General W. H. Northam CB wrote:

'It is considered that this offer should be accepted and the medal or prize should be awarded to a man holding the rating of Sick Berth Steward, the Depots Portsmouth, Plymouth and Chatham taking the prize annually in turn. The decision as to whom the award should be made to rest with the Surgeon Rear Admiral at the respective hospital viz. Haslar, Plymouth or Chatham as the case may be.'

Thus the principle was established, but it proved to be a very long time before the ever growing file ceased circulation and the first medal was awarded! Some of the more interesting comments have been extracted from the voluminous file.

11.5.19

Skinner of N Branch wrote that if the MDG's suggestion was approved the claims of all Sick Berth Stewards attached to the Port Division should come under review. He seemed unhappy about the award of a medal which would not be worn, and pressed the case for a money prize. He attached a War Office paper dated 6th May 1912 covering such awards to the Army and suggested that the donor might be asked whether he would prefer the proceeds from his gift to be used as a money prize. He also pointed out that a deed would have to be drawn up and a name given to the award.

12.5.19 The Assistant Secretary to the Admiralty J. Anderson CB MVC concurred that a money prize was preferable to a medal.

Further circulation for comments ensued and on 19th May a letter from the Assistant Secretary Finance was sent to the donor conveying thanks from the Lords Commissioners accepting the offer.

29.5.19 A further letter was sent to FWC enclosing copy of a draft Admiralty Monthly Order for future promulgation, and asking for any suggested alterations to it. Again there was an enquiry as to whether FWC would prefer a money prize or a medal.

The donor fended this off by leaving the matter of the medal to the discretion of Their Lordships, and sent a cheque for £100. This was duly received by the Registry, sent to the Asst' Sec' Finance for endorsement and received by the Acc't Generals Dept. Further circulation of an ever growing file followed discussing the difficulties of awarding the medal fairly, whether or not it should be of silver and how the cost of design, die and annual award could be met from interest on the sum invested. At this stage the Admiralty Solicitor wished the Treasury to be involved.

18th October 1919. Donor was asked to call at Admiralty and a letter was sent to the Royal Mint re cost of striking the medal.

Meanwhile in August Admiralty Monthly Order 2445 (N22278) 16.7.19 was promulgated which read:-

1. A retired Naval Officer who wishes to remain anonymous has generously offered the sum of £100 to provide for the annual award of a medal to one of the Sick Berth Staff in the RN for zeal and efficiency shown in the discharge of his duties during the preceding year.

2. It has been decided to accept this offer and to employ the proceeds of the above sum in providing a medal to be called the Sick Berth Steward's Efficiency Medal which will be awarded to men holding the rating of Sick Berth Steward in Portsmouth, Devonport and Chatham Port Divisions in successive years.

3. Selection for the award of the medal will be made as follows.

a. Senior Medical Officers of HM Ships and Depots and of RN Hospitals and Hospital Ships will be entitled to forward (through the Captains and Flag Officers under whom they are serving) to the Surgeon Rear Admiral of the RN Hospitals Haslar, Plymouth and Chatham (according to which Port Division is entitled to the medal

for the year) the names of Sick Berth Stewards whom they recommend for the medal. Each recommendation is to be accompanied by a copy of the men's Service Certificate and S457 together with a statement of any special services rendered during the year. Recommendations must reach the Surgeon Rear Admiral not later than 1st December.
b. The SRA will select and place in order of merit the three candidates whom he considers most worthy of the medal, and will forward all recommendations received, together with his selection to MDG.
c. The MDG will report to the Admiralty the name, rating, and official number of the Sick Berth Steward to whom he recommends the medal should be awarded.
4. The first selection for the medal will be made by SRA at Haslar on 1st January 1920 to a Sick Berth Steward of Portsmouth Port Division. The award on January 1st 1921 will be made to Devonport Port Division and on Jan 1st 1922 to Chatham Port Division and thereafter in rotation. The medal is not to be worn.

All now appeared to be ready for the first presentation, but it was not to be.

20.10.1919.   A letter was sent to FWC requesting him to call at Admiralty to discuss outstanding details of production and design, and to look over a draft copy of the declaration of Trust.

This he did and shortly afterwards FWC forwarded a second cheque for £100 bringing the total to £200.

3.11.1919.   Letter from FWC to Plummer, Principal Clerk.
'Suggestions for specifications.
1.   Not less than a penny in size (in case).
2.   Edge to project in order to receive the date and name of recipient on rim.
3.   Substance should be 9ct gold if cost of 18ct will not permit.
4.   On one side of the medal there should be near the edge the words Naval Sick Berth Steward's Efficiency Medal. This should also depict a small part of a ward of a Naval Hospital Ship with Naval Medical Officer and Sick Berth Steward attending a wounded man on a bed or stretcher, suggesting the necessity for loyal co-operation of Sick Berth Staff and Medical Staff.
5.   The other side of the medal should show a Naval Hospital Ship say the *Soudan*, with other war vessels in the distance with the word below 'Ready'. The medal should be complete and as each is awarded the name of the recipient and the date should be engraved on the edge as before mentioned.
6.   Should £200 in all be insufficient to meet present and future costs of the medal as above a silver gilt medal to last 20 years might be provided but not otherwise.'

14.11.19   Head of N Branch to MDG. A letter querying the design for reverse. He pointed out that the only distinguishing signs of a Hospital ship were a green or red band on the hull and a Red Cross flag. Was this flown at the mainmast head, if not where? Could he loan a photograph of a Hospital Ship preferably the *Soudan*? The design would be so small that it would probably show little more than the stern showing Red Cross Flag.

MDG loaned a photo of the *Soudan*. In the same month The Master of the Royal Mint was approached and asked to undertake production. He was also asked to cost expense of design, die, case and annual medal.

Reply stated that the designs were very elaborate, sums available were insufficient. Design of four medals for the RAF (presumably the DFC AFC DFM AFM) cost 150 guineas each and reverse of British War Medal £500.

Annual charge for medal bullion engraving and case would be £2-£3 in 18ct gold, 25/- in 9ct which was difficult to work or 10/- in silver gilt. He suggested the latter when a larger medal could be struck for £20 invested at 5 per cent leaving £80 available for legal fees and artist. A much larger investment would be required for gold. He suggested naming a definite sum to be awarded for two model designs and an approach to Sir Cecil Harcourt Smith, Director Victoria and Albert Museum to name two possible designers.

Throughout December the file circulated, one minute pointed out that Red Cross flag was flown from the foremast head and not from the mainmast.

In January 1920 there appeared a minor crisis. FWC wrote that it was over six months since he had written his first cheque, and this had not been presented, he had therefore stopped the cheque and another one issued. There was a flutter in the Civil Service dovecotes at Admiralty, and a very formal letter 'I am directed by the Lords Commissioners of Admiralty to inform you . . . ' was sent to FWC informing him that there was no trace of the letter or cheque having been received!

For the next six months letters were circulating the Departments, to FWC, the Mint, The V and A Museum and the British Museum, whose Directors had been consulted on design. Two designers Preston and Stabler submitted drawings, Preston in the form of plaster models and Stabler in the form of a sketch. The two Directors found it difficult to compare a drawing with a model. Others preferred Preston's design but Stabler's lettering. N Branch criticised the rings on the Medical Officer's jacket (probably because curls had just been approved for the gold braid rings of Medical Officers) and that the SBS was wearing his Red Cross on the left and not the right arm. The V and A Director had stated that the specification was probably suitable for a large painting, contained too much detail and 'leaves us rather hopeless, no self respecting medallic artist would be willing to touch the matter!.'

The very patient donor responded to a suggestion for revised instructions that he was happy to look upon his suggestions as broad detail only and to leave it to the discretion of the designer. Eventually each designer was paid £10, Preston's design was accepted and he was paid a further £40, and was asked to modify the uniforms and the lettering.

By July 1920 some progress was evident, large plaster models had been received and working models were forwarded to the Mint. Meanwhile, the file, growing ever larger was still doing its rounds of the departments concerned. £140 remained for investment, it was suggested that interest would permit a larger medal after defraying legal expenses and stamp duty. The ever patient FWC came up with the offer of a further £50. In November the Mint suggested that annual interest of £7 on a £140 investment would permit an 18ct gold penny sized award, the thickness of which could be varied from year to year according to the cost of bullion.

5.12.20   A further burst of bumph circulated the offices of the Second Sea Lord, the Fourth Sea Lord, MDG, N Branch and their Principal Secretaries. Some one had suddenly noticed that the title Sick Berth Steward had been changed to Sick Berth Petty Officer on 5th August. No action had been taken, and as a result the models had been sent to the Mint bearing the old title. It was noted by the Second Sea Lord, Vice Admiral Sir Henry Oliver KCB KCMG CVO, that seventeen months had elapsed.

Over to the Mint, whose Deputy Controller stated that electro types had already been prepared, and that they would make no alterations to the lettering without reference to the artist.

In January 1921 a letter to Preston revealed that the matrix had been destroyed and the cost of preparing a new revised model would be £12–£15. Further correspondence ensued, and by the end of February 1921 the Mint was requested to proceed with production, with a slight reduction in the medal's thickness.

The peace and calm in the corridors of Power reigned again and for four months not a letter was written.

In July 1921 FWC was requested to call at the Admiralty to sign a Trust Deed drawn up by the Admiralty Solicitor. This document ran into three foolscap pages and was signed on behalf of Admiralty by Rear Admiral A. D. Boyle, (the famous Paddy Boyle, who as CinC Med Fleet in 1926 sent the famous signal 'Hold the fort for I am coming' to his counterpart in China, in action with the Chinese off Nanking. He was recalled from retirement during the second world war and took command of RN Ships in the invasion and evacuation of Norway).

The signature of the other Commissioner was that of the Second Sea Lord Vice Admiral Sir H. F. Oliver, both signatures being witnessed by

Paymaster Officers of their staffs. FWC's signature was witnessed by his Bank Manager.

One could well think that this finally closed the file, but it was not to be. The Accountant General started the ball rolling once more by circulating a memo in August 1921 pointing out that the balance was £126 less 10/- Stamp duty and that medals were due for 1920, 1921 and shortly 1922. The annual cost of production would be £6.4.10d and allowing for the cost of the three medals, interest on £106.5.6d would be insufficient to cover future issues. Therefore £125 should be invested, and no additional medals issued until adequate funds accumulated.

A final decision was made to retain £15 for the first two medals now due, to invest £110 as suggested to bring in interest of £6 per annum.

In August 1922 it was pointed out that the annual interest was £6.0.10d and that the cost of the 1922 medal should not exceed this sum.

The first Efficiency Medal was awarded almost two years after the donor first wrote to Admiralty, and even that did not proceed without a hitch. On 22nd June 1921 the SRA at Haslar wrote to MDG stating that the 1919 award was due to SBPO Lowe and could this be forwarded.

On 7th September the Superintendent Royal Mint stated that medal was ready for inscription. Details of recipient were forwarded, but only after a thorough search of Admiralty Depts, there was no trace of the medal and a phone call to the Mint established that there was a delay in its production (by no means the first!).

The current cost of the medal (1984) is £60, and in order to cope with ever increasing costs an appeal for funds was made just after the Second World War. In 1983 a Serving Surgeon Commander made a donation of £200 in order that the award may continue.

Footnote A research into the Career of FWC has revealed the following details:

20.2.1888 Appointed Surgeon Royal Navy.

The following appointments are listed:

22. 2.88. HMS *Duke of Wellington* Flagship Portsmouth for RNH Haslar.

6. 7.88. HMS *Indus* Flagship Admiral Superintendent Devonport, lent *Pilot* for training season. (HMS *Pilot* was a 510 ton full rigged brig, tender to *Impregnable* and used for Boys training).

24. 6.90. HMS *Curlew*, Channel Squadron.

14. 5.92. HMS *Vivid* for RNB Devonport, lent HMS *Swiftsure*, Port Guardship Devonport.

17.10.93. HMS *Ramillies* Flagship Meditteranean Fleet.

25.10.94. HMS *Vivid* for RNB Devonport.

14. 1.96. HMS *Penguin* Survey vessel, recommissioned at Sydney.

In the Navy Lists of April and July 1897 he appeared on Active List without appointment, possibly on passage to UK in a merchant ship.

In October 1897 he was placed on the Retired List with seniority 22.2.1888. He did not appear again on the Active List and judging by his remarks in his first letter to the Admiralty he must have been an old man in 1919.

He did not serve in HMHS *Soudan*.

Records of personnel who have received this award.

Year	Rate	Name	Number
1920	SBPO	LOWE E. W.	351127
1922	SBPO	FORREST J. J.	351237
1924	SBPO	HOARE B. J.	351667
1925	SBPO	MITCHENOR F.	M1949
1927	SBPO	HEATH G. W.	M915
1931	SBPO	PECK S. L.	C/M21243
1932	SBPO	ANDREWS J. W.	P/M5177
1933 ·	SBPO	GUNN A. E.	D/M 5364
1934	SBPO	FARNHAM A. J.	C/M35996
1935	SBPO	ISHAM T. C.	P/M25119
1936	SBPO	HEWITT W. E.	D/M35699
1938	SBPO	LANGFORD A. E. H.	P/M20822
1947	SBPO	DUNCAN J.	P/MX57251
1948	SBPO	GAY H. E.	D/MX54723
1949	SBPO	GEORGE E. J.	C/MX46650
1956	SBPO	BELLENGER C.	P/MX61699
1957	SBPO	CONN J.	D/MX73205
1963	SBPO	STOWE J. H.	P/MX55836
1966	No award		
1974	No award		
1975	POMA	KILLICK	M968937E
1976	No award		
1977	POMA	SARGEANT M. C.	M982413C
1978	POMA	HARRIS G. F.	D097946W
1979	POMA	COCHRANE J. C.	D050890X
1980	POMA	BROWN I.	D089369N
1981	POMA	DOUGLAS I. E.	D089800E
1982	POMA	GERRELL F. J.	D1270357
1983	POMA	CURRIE D. E.	D129539V

CHAPTER SEVEN

Reminiscences

No booklet of this nature would be complete without the inclusion of some reminiscences from former members of the Medical Services and Sick Berth Branch of the Royal Navy. To this end an appeal was made via the local press and radio stations serving the areas of the three naval home ports.

The response was far greater than expected – contributions came by post, on tapes, via the telephone and even by personal interviews, in fact, information accumulated to such an extent that were everything reported, a separate booklet would be necessary. Where relevant to the earlier text references have been made to some of the material received and what follows in this chapter are abridged accounts from named personalities.

These have been selected purely on the grounds of a chronological survey of the history of the branch so that a cross section of experiences may be given. All reports, in their unabridged states have been deposited in the archives of Haslar's Medical Museum where they will form a most useful pool of information for future researchers.

A Victorian SBA

W. J. K. Swailes

The account about the above ex-member of the Branch has been given both in correspondence and taped conversation by his son, now a sprightly 78 years young who lives in Devon. He supplied the information from his father's letters and memories of his conversations.

'My father ran away from home to join the Navy in 1892, first as a Steward and then transferring to the Sick Berth Branch. Father often mentioned that cases of scurvy still existed and in a letter he wrote, whilst serving in a warship overseas, he mentioned that the young Assistant Fleet Surgeon on board used to ensure that their ship's company had a reasonable supply of fresh vegetables in the Tropics. This he achieved by soaking several blankets in water and then emptying marrowfat peas on them and exposing the blankets to the strong sunshine. Germination quickly occurred and the green shoots that grew were used as vegetables. SBA Swailes served in the latter part of the 19th century on the New Zealand station in HMS *Taranga*, a sail and steam-vessel, usually using engines when entering or leaving harbour, but once at sea, the propeller was drawn inboard, the funnel lowered and sails hoisted. Whilst sailing around the Pacific Islands father visited the camps of many missionaries in areas where the natives still practised cannibalism. He served aboard HMS *Lapwing* (also sail and steam) in the Persian Gulf and did a long refit in Bombay. Thereafter he did commissions in HM Ships *Carnarvon* and *Achilles* before going to the RN Hospital at Portland from where he took his service pension. He continued to work there in the Dockyard Surgery in a civilian capacity throughout the First World War and often spoke of an incident which was as mysterious in 1917 as it is to this day.

Apparently the British Armed Yacht *Lorna Doone* had a skirmish with a German U-Boat on the surface off Chesil Beach. The submarine dived, disappearing beneath the waves but shortly afterwards the dead body of a German naval officer was recovered from the water in the area where the U-Boat had surfaced. The corpse was taken into Portland's Dockyard Surgery where it was examined and from all accounts, it had not been in the sea very long. In one of the uniform pockets, letters were found which revealed the officer's name which was the same on the bill of a Bournemouth hotel also found in a pocket where according to the date given, the officer had stayed a few weeks previously. How this could have occurred was never revealed, though my father did question the authorities'.

With a Sick Berth Steward on the Western Front in 1916

George Coker, a Sick Berth Steward, at the outbreak of World War 1 was about to go to pension when war occurred after serving in what he thought was his last ship, the Royal Yacht *Victoria and Albert*. Instead, on August 19th, he found himself drafted to HMS *Agincourt* at Scapa Flow where Admiral Jellicoe with his battle cruisers lay in waiting for the German Fleet to emerge from its home ports, an event which did not really happen until May 1916 when the Battle of Jutland was fought.

It was thus a long wait and meanwhile the Allied Armies in France held a line against the German armies stretching from almost the Channel Coast to the Alps, a distance of around 350 miles with 1½ million men on a very flexible front that at times remained stable but was subject to dispute and bitter fighting by both sides. To give the waiting sailors at Scapa Flow some idea of the conditions their comrades in arms were experiencing, an Admiralty Fleet Order issued in January 1916 informed naval personnel that a few volunteer parties would be taken to front lines trenches to see for themselves what Allied Soldiers experienced. One such volunteer was George Coker who spent some time with the Coldstream Guards in front line trenches at Ypres, commonly referred to by the British Tommy as 'Wipers'. Just before he arrived, this part of the front line had received its first gas attack which had killed many Canadian soldiers who were then occupying part of the front line section. Already in 1915, the town, about 25 miles South of Ostend was in ruins from the daily shelling by German Artillery but throughout the war it was to remain one of the focal points of the struggle and the scene of many British casualties. To George Coker it proved a most moving experience and on his return he wrote in diary form notes about his visit. This is really an understatement for the notes, typewritten on the Sick Bay's machine, occupy 21 pages of large size Naval S575 forms which are marked TELEGRAM (Established March 1880 Revised April 1912).

Very fortunately his account was preserved by his son who very kindly forwarded it to the RN Hospital, Haslar, for inclusion in this booklet. The whole account makes compelling reading and it is a pity it cannot be reproduced in full but space is limited and there are so many incidents to relate from other ex-members of the branch. What follows therefore are purely, disjointed extracts, but they are completely unaltered.

'In London we proceeded to the Union Jack Club where we were given a meat tea and issued with khaki uniforms, long india rubber waders, and emergency rations on the Army scale of 1 lb tin of corned beef, 1 lb biscuits and a small tin containing tea, sugar and 2 oxo cubes.

We reached Poperinghe at 10.30 am. where a halt was made. The military activity became more pronounced, cars of all descriptions and vehicles, motor, horse and mule were dashing to and fro in an endless stream, the traffic being regulated by a military policeman. A light railway traverses the heart of the city square from side to side and now and again a train would puff bravely across. The town shows striking evidence of bombardment, pavements uprooted, lamp standards lying down and various buildings without a roof but some shops were patched up with wire netting and many carried on business as usual.

On the outskirts of Ypres we left the lorries and proceeded on foot but with duffle coats, carrying our packs and respirators and being told we had 3 miles to cover we became too warm to be comfortable.

As we were going to the trenches that afternoon, we were told to keep to the trench boards otherwise no one could keep a foot hold in the thick mud and a slide into the canal would be a certainty.

We then prepared for moving at dusk. We were ordered to 'off boots' and 'on waders' our gas masks were examined, eye glasses screwed firm, valve and mouth piece working properly and every item checked by an officer. By day, gas can be seen approaching in a cloud, by night, it is detected by a faint sweetish smell closely akin to the taste of new cider.

In the trenches there is just enough room for one to move along. We were now in the firing lane of the Ypres salient and our party was distributed in pairs, a seaman Petty Officer and myself had to go to the other side of the road through a small tunnel and there we were allocated to a sergeant of the Coldstream Guards. The trench was wet, dark and muddy and feeling pretty cold I thought I would move to a dug-out I had spotted earlier, the entrance was low and I crawled in hoping to get some sleep but the rats were too inquisitive and I did not appreciate their attentions. Wounded receive first aid treatment and are then passed down the line on stretchers or sitting stretchers by communication trenches to the base to be seen by the MO. If there are no communication trenches they remain where they are with temporary dressings until nightfall when they are moved. Moving them in daylight attracts a hail of shrapnel, whizz-bangs or machine gun fire.

The fatigue party cleans the sanitary arrangements (plank and buckets) each night by liberal use of chloride of lime.

In repairing broken trenches, men are subject to constant gunfire but they consider themselves lucky if they get a simple bullet wound which they term a 'Blighty' as it will no doubt mean leave at home.

Just ahead of our position were the old Canadian dug outs and trenches lost by the first gas attack in which the bodies of the Canadians are still lying there with their heads covered by sand bags, the Germans stop by their fire any attempt by our people to bury them.

We were bombarded throughout the night but my feet being like ice and my legs numbed to the knees. I was driven out of my billet by the cold. Our soldiers' opinions of the German fire power is that it is very effective both as regards artillery and small arms. Early in the morning, the 26th, a shower of whizz-bangs was received, when one had to look pretty smart and get under the lee of sandbags to shelter from metal splinters and a bombardment from hill "60" on our position. Casualties today – 4 killed, 2 wounded. The new helmets are heavy (about 2 lbs) and give the men headaches if worn more than 3 hours on end, as far as they are available at present they are worn in the proportion of 1 in 4. We sat round while 24 hr rations were served, then supper of bread and cheese and ½ pint of 1 in 3 rum.

Full speed was ordered so that we could catch the mail boat at Boulonge at 3.15 p.m. We must have looked like a crowd of duffle coated bearded tramps.

There were no casualties in my platoon but most of the others had, one PO was in a dug out with 2 soldiers when a shell came and buried the lot, when dug out the PO was still alive, but badly suffering with shell shock, the soldiers were killed. It is a hard life in the Front Line'.

Signed George Coker
Sick Berth Steward

April 1916.

St. John Ambulance Brigade Sick Berth Reserves 1914

An Account of my father's service by: T. Henthorn

My father joined the St. John Ambulance Brigade Reserve in 1913. He went to Torquay with them in June 1914 and did training in HMS *Queen Elizabeth* which was lying off Torbay. With the onset of war in 1914 he was called up for service on 2nd August and reported to Chatham Barracks the next day. He was one of the first party of 12 men from the Oldham area to do so. Some of his comrades sailed for the South Atlantic and were in the Falkland Isles victory in December. My father was drafted to the China Station on the 7th August. I am not sure exactly what happened but he called at such places as Hong Kong, Weihaiwei and Port Arthur and was en route for Japan when the ship was recalled to Malta because of the casualties from the Dardanelles Campaign and he joined the RN Hospital, Bighi. Later he served in HMS *Egmont*. From his diary he mentions various hospital ships he either served in or visited – HMHS *Guildford Castle, Nevasa* and *Delta*. Some of his diary extracts are relevant.

June 5th 1916 Went aboard HMHS *Delta* with 11 cases. Ship looked very different after the alterations. It now has 600 cots. When I was on board it only had 180. Had a nice trip out wearing my whites and tropical helmet. Returned ashore on the Fleet Surgeon's boat.

August 6th 1916 The Australian's were fighting British servicemen with knives and bottles. Police had a rough time. Guard called out with fixed bayonets to stop the fighting.

March 16th 1917 Departed Malta in troop ship SS *Cameronia* for 2 days voyage to Marseilles with 3000 men on board, arrived 18th March, stayed on board overnight.

March 19th 1917 Boarded train across France to Le Havre.

March 21st 1917 Marched to the Dock's Rest Camp and stayed 1 day.

March 22nd 1917 Caught midnight boat SS *Archangel* to Southampton, arrived Southampton 0700. Then by rail to London and Chatham arriving there at 2100.

March 24th 1917 Left Chatham Barracks for 13 days leave. Returned Chatham after leave and drafted to Melville Barracks, Brompton, the overflow annexe of the RN Hospital 'Gillingham'.

September 3rd 1917 Air Raid on Chatham Barracks. Drill Hall hit. Many killed and wounded. Later given as 107 killed, 86 wounded.

September 18th 1918 Won Medal for playing cricket.

September 30th 1918 1914, 1915 and 1916. Chevrons awarded.

November 11th 1918 Peace Armistice signed. Went to London.

April 8th 1919 Could have been demobbed today but agreed to stay on for a short while.

April 24th 1919 12 SBA's leave for Russia?

June 13th 1919 Attended Naval Memorial Service at St Pauls, London. Lunched at the Guildhall. Service was attended by King and Queen, Admiral Wemyss, Churchill, etc.

July 19th 1919 Peace celebrations. Went to Party in London.

July 21st 1919 Stationed at St. Mary's island isolation camp, Chatham Dockyard.

July 28th 1919 Duty at Pembroke II.

August 26th 1919 Drew my gratuity – £29.

August 27th 1919 Drew my 1914–1915 Medal ribbons.

August 30th 1919 Escort Duty – Left RNH Gillingham 0630. Arrived Newcastle 1625. Patient refused admission proceeded to Morpeth Asylum, 15 miles away, to hand over patient.

August 31st 1919 Returned to RNH Gillingham. Claimed £1.4s.6d (£1.225) expenses for the two of us.

September 25th 1919 Name goes forward for demob'.

September 27th 1919 Train strike. All demob' stopped.

September 28–30th 1919 All leave stopped.

October 2nd 1919 Proceeded on 'demob' leave.

P.S. A few things father mentioned to me years ago.

He spoke of having to go out to the gun batteries on the old forts by the River Medway for hygiene inspections, fumigations etc.

When he first reported for duty at Chatham they did not recognise the uniform he was wearing which was part naval and part St. John Ambulance Brigade and he must have dressed the same when in China as some thought it was a Russian uniform until he told them otherwise. Sennet hats were issued to them and he said the only good thing about them was they were excellent when stationed in China for catching butterflies.

My father died in July 1982 just 3 months short of his 88th Birthday, he was always interested in the Services having joined the Church Lad's Brigade in 1910, was an all-rounder in games and helped to win the shield and medals for Chatham Division in September 1918.

He worked after the war as a civilian at Chatham Barracks and during the Second World War he worked at the war time Cookham Camp Borstal, Rochester. Later he was employed in the surgery in Chatham Dockyard until he retired in 1962.

From Novice Monk to SBA and Naval Executive Officer

Thumb nail sketch of the naval career of former SBPO S. E. Pollett

'In 1921 I was novice monk at the House of the Sacred Mission in Nottinghamshire but because of the sudden death of my step-father I was obliged to leave for civilian life to help with family finances.

Securing a berth as a deck boy on TSS *Port Napier* in which I did two trips to Australia and New Zealand and between trips I returned to my religious house and took my place in the Society.

Depressions were also fashionable in the 1920's and when my ship was laid up with scores of others I decided to join the Navy as a Seaman. Not so said the recruiting CPO who with a generous amount of guile shanghaied me into the Sick Berth Branch. This was in June 1923. As far as I know, I was the first and only Novice monk to join as a SB rating. My most poignant memory of probationer's days at Chatham RN Hospital is that of hunger. We were not allowed to incur Mess Bills and we had to survive on standard rations and allowances. One of our two Instructing Petty Officers ran a motor cycle and side-car and we jokingly maintained that it was run on our Messing Allowances. When we attending Cooking for the Sick at the Barracks Cookery School we used to snatch a handful of the prepared food as we passed through. When we came to our Cookery Practical examination my friend and I had to make a rice pudding with egg. When it was cooked we were so overcome with hunger, we ate the offering so that when the Cookery Officer came to inspect our concoctions, we had none for him to inspect – nevertheless we both passed the examination! Whilst under training I won a Novices' Competition in a Boxing Programme at Chatham Barracks and was drafted to the Barracks Gymnasium to train as one of the Depot Boxing Team with such well known naval boxers as Stoker PO Bob Spiller, Royal Marine Trinder, Leading Seaman Evans and others. The hospital authorities stopped my draft and I had to train in my own free time so when the team visited Portsmouth for the Inter-Port Championships I went as First Reserve Bantam or Featherweight but I failed to make the weight of 8 stone 6 lbs, I was so ill prepared. At the time of my training as an SBA the instruction was reputed to be of a very high standard, especially as the State Registered Nurse was not much in vogue and nurses from St. Bartholomew's Hospital were always trying to get copies of our Training Manual.

Apart from leaves spent at my Religious House and my boxing, life was not very exciting and at my own request I was released from my Novitiate in 1926, married in 1927 and purchased my discharge from the Navy in 1928 for £36. I left on Friday August 17th. Started work on August 24th and never lost a day afterwards. In 1938 or early 1939 when Civil Defence Forces were being mobilised, I volunteered to return to the Navy and was called up in September 1939 and quickly realised that the Navy I left in 1928 was not the same one I rejoined in 1939, when the 'Crusher' at the Royal Naval Barracks referred to me as 'That Gentleman, there'. My first ship was a 'Q' ship. Lots have been written about 'Q' Ships in World War 1, but there were a couple in World War II. The one I commissioned at Middlesbrough in December 1940 was the Booth Line TSS *Crispin* subsequently to become HMS *Crispin*. From Middlesbrough we sailed to Glasgow to have our armament installed, two 4' guns, one forward and one aft. The guns were concealed in steel casings painted to look like deck cargo of tractor packing cases, and believe it or not, on the sides were painted in large black letters 'MORRIS OF MANCHESTER' to mislead the Germans in case they did not know that Morris's were in Oxford and Cowley. The idea was that we should be at the rear of the convoy, the 'lame' duck which could not maintain sufficient speed and thus act as 'bait' to German Fokker Wolf Condor aircraft and when attacked we would open up our 'packing cases' and shoot down the aircraft. We all wore civilian clothes and flew the Red Ensign, except when in port when we donned naval uniform and hoisted the White Ensign. We accompanied a convoy to about 500 miles west of Ireland, then made a rendezvous with another and followed it home. On our third trip we were torpedoed and took an hour to sink though a gale was raging. Over 20 were lost by drowning, some because they could not successfully jump the gap from the tossing lifeboat to the destroyer that picked us up from the cold waters some 4 hours later. Just before I abandoned ship I went down to the Sick Bay to collect anything I could conveniently carry. These items were a bottle of the Sick Bay's Medicinal Brandy which I thought would be an antidote to the cold in the lifeboat, but to avoid any trouble I handed it to the Merchant Navy Officer in charge of the lifeboat because some of the men had raided the rum store and the NAAFI and were already drunk.

Our Captain was Commander Maloney RNR who went down with his ship together with the Yeoman of Signals. My other messmates were Special Service Volunteers whose pay was 4/6d. daily (22½p), double my own! It really was an awful sight, seeing one's ship slowly but surely sinking silhouetted against the skyline. Rescued by HMS *Harvester* I was given survivor's leave and then drafted to HMHS *Oxfordshire*, the base hospital ship in Freetown, Sierra Leone. The Surgeons on board were always grateful for any surgery they could 'drum-up' to keep their hands-in as there did not seem to be an awful lot about. SBA Commerford, known as 'Ginger' was persuaded to have both small toes amputated because they overlapped the next toe and to commemorate the event I wrote the following jingle:

A shock it was when I was told
To walk with ease when I am old
To stand with dignity and grace
No anguished furrow on my face
'twere best to lose the least of ten
The shortest limb despised by men
The little toe, phalange of scorn
That plinth for such a splendid corn
I did regard you in my youth
As less important than a tooth
And squeezed you tightly in my shoe
Only clods give space to you
Nor heed your plea each frosty night
A chilblain chose you for a site
My vanity, sadly, knew no fence
And now to me you are past tense

Surgeon Captain Maxwell and Commissioned Wardmaster Titmus recommended me for a Commission, and I was sent home in December 1943. I was then a two-badge SBPO and my erstwhile mates thought they had hallucinations when they saw me drilling conscripts on the Parade Ground. I became an Executive Sub-Lieutenant at HMS *King Alfred* from where I was appointed to the RN College for a Navigation Course.

Then I joined a Minesweeper as Anti-Submarine Control Officer and as a sideline, became Wardroom Wine Caterer. Our main employment was sweeping cross-channel routes for supplies to the Normandy invasion which finally culminated in helping to sweep a clear passage for Prince Olaf's return to Norway.

Quite a career for a Noviate Monk cum SBA and Executive Officer. My initial contemporaries could have provided excellent information but I suppose most are now dead. I'm 79 this year. Best of luck to the Branch and the book.'

S. E. POLLETT

Chatham Training in the 1930's

A few reminiscences from ex-SBA Jack Fletcher

Jack Fletcher gave a most comprehensive account of training as a probationer at RNH Chatham much of which he will recognise from the text in this booklet. In common with similar comments from other former SBA's he remarked that though the Service Authorities did not discourage personnel from taking the Nursing Examinations for State

Registration, they did not encourage those who were keen. He mentioned that the examinations were held in London and that if an SBA wished to sit them, he had to apply for special leave but any expenses incurred in connection with travel and fees, were the Attendant's personal responsibility. A few incidents about Chatham he well remembers.

The most outstanding one concerns the murder there in 1934, of a Chief Petty Officer Palmer. Apparently he was serving aboard a 15″ gun monitor, HMS *Marshall Soult*, a veteran of the First World War which was in the Reserve Fleet, Chatham. One evening a CPO Brigstock visited the ship saying to the Royal Marine sentry that he wanted to see CPO Palmer and being admitted, he disappeared to the CPO's Mess. Later he emerged holding a blood stained razor having told the sentry that he had killed CPO Palmer. The body was brought to the mortuary of the hospital where a post mortem was immediately held pending an inquest. It appeared that the head was almost severed from the body and the severity of the attack was the source of much comment. CPO Brigstock was convicted and eventually hanged but there was even greater comment about the conviction for it did appear in the evidence at the trial that the murderer had been mentally unstable for some considerable time. A minor event he also recalls was an influenza epidemic when some 60 naval cadets from an adjacent school were admitted as patients. The hospital was pretty full and they were accommodated in the Sick Berth Probationer's Instruction Ward where, in anticipation of this influx, the probationers had hastily prepared extra accommodation even in the corridors of their ward.

The news of this work reached the ears of the renowned Admiral David Evans or 'Evans of the Broke' as he was known familiarly. With his swashbuckling manner and uniform cap jauntily worn with the peak to one side, and the Commander-in-Chief of the Grand Fleet who accepted the German surrender in November 1918, he was a personality well known and respected by the British public. So when it was heard that he intended to visit Chatham Hospital and thank the Probationers for their kindness, it caused great excitement. He did pay a visit and they were introduced to him.

Jack Fletcher, in concluding his reminiscences, remarked that whilst at Chatham, trials concerning the use of the antiseptic 'Dettol' were being conducted and probationers so frequently employed with dressings of varied types were sick of the smell of Dettol in fact Jack has only to get a whiff of the antiseptic today to take his mind back to those early days.

Letter from Mrs C. Buddin wife of the late SBPO C. E. Buddin MBE DSM

As I was married to one of the staff trained at RN Hospital, Haslar I shared many items of interest in various departments. For instance when he was duty weekend in N. Block (Mental Block) in the 1930's. I used to go over to Haslar and was let in through a lockable gate to 'N' Block, spend the evening playing 'Uckers' with the staff and sharing their tea of watercress sandwiches and cakes with the knowledge that if an officer appeared I would be put in the boot cupboard. When it was time for me to leave, I was let out through the 'Camel's eye' in the gate. One of the patients who was a naval blacksmith used to offer the staff, yachts, jewels, money etc., if they would free him fron 'N' Block. He refused to take medicine unless my husband gave it to him and even threw it over the Doctor in the absence of my husband. On one occasion a patient did get out and climbed up the surrounding wall. On being told to come down, he did just that and landed on top of the SBA and put him 'out'. Dances used to be held in the hospital in the Errol Hall monthly and were well attended, people from outside being transported home by ambulance for which we paid a small fee. At one of these events I won one of the first Premium Bonds issued but it did not prove to be a lucky one. My husband had 7 medals at the time of his death and a 'Mention in Despatches'. During the war being on convoys all the time, he had no time to sit for the 'Chiefs' exam, however, he was on loan to another ship with that acting rank and drew the pay for same in the HMS *Teal*. When he was finally sent home from Malta for his wounds to heal, everything possible was done to faciliate my daily visits – i.e. use of the Haslar boat and a member of the staff waiting for me with my husband in a wheelchair ready for me to take him round the grounds. I always found that whenever members of the staff met, there was always an 'espirit de corps', jokes and talk of Haslar were always to the fore. I have photographs of dinner dances at Haslar at which we attended.

Yours sincerely

C. BUDDIN (Mrs)

Note Mrs C. Buddin was 75 years of age in 1983. Her late husband was badly wounded in a Malta Convoy during the Second World War, and was invalided to Haslar where his right leg was amputated. He received the DSM for his most courageous work during Convoys. Leaving the Navy he did voluntary work with BLESMA and was employed as local Secretary to the RNBT for 18 years. He also founded the Portsmouth Branch of BLESMA and served on the management Board of their Southsea home. For his wonderful public spirited services he was awarded the MBE. He died in 1971

West River Patrol in South China 1937–1939

An account supplied by former SBPO (X) Jack Fitch who served in the RN from 1933–47 and who was Secretary to the RN Sick Berth and Medical Branch Staff Association at the time of its dissolutio-

This patrol was instituted in 1840 after the Opium War in China and was carried out between Canton and Hong Kong by five gunboats which had routine interchangeable patrol areas between the two places. A Medical Officer was appointed for the whole patrol and there was a Sick Bay man in each ship's complement. These gunboats, together with another dozen similar craft serving on the Yangtse river were in some respects unique. They were the only naval vessels which included in their action stations the order to 'Repel boarders' and in common with sloops in the Persian Gulf, they were also allowed to keep beer on board for sale to ships' companies, an added bonus to the gratuitous daily issue of rum. In the task of minimising the trafficking of opium on the river, life was never dull, boarding parties were sent to search suspicious craft and frequently Chinese pirates were caught and handed over to the local police. The change round of patrol areas meant that approximately once each month, the complement of every gunboat had leave in Hong Kong. Each vessel despite its small displacement was armed, usually with 3″ guns, Lewis guns and 2 pounders. Designed to have a small draught of water usually no more than 4 ft, they were ideal boats for patrolling some 1000 miles of waters on the West River and its delta. As on certain stretches they had to pass beneath telephone wires that bridged the river, the evolution known as 'Striking the topmast' was well known.

Life in the Sickbay was reasonably quiet, most attendances being for minor injuries and the occasional case of malaria and dysentery. Sometimes there was an S 576 case, the inevitable result of a 'run ashore' by someone with a lady of easy virtue in Wanchai, the red-light area of Hong Kong. One problem which affected everyone was the rationing of water, one bucket-full per man per day drawn from the ship's condenser. Half of this was for drinking, the other half for personal toilet use and washing clothes. This was necessary because the river water was so heavily polluted and it was not uncommon to see the bloated carcases of animals and on occasions a human corpse, floating down the river towards the sea on the 8 knot current. River water was only used for scrubbing the decks and the only opportunity for a bathe was in a pool formed at the foot of a waterfall some 5 miles inland. Leave for this purpose was always granted which did mean a real bathe once monthly when the ship was in this vicinty. Jack Fitch served in the *Seamew* which was built in 1927 and the only boat on the West river equipped with geared turbines, which gave her a speed of 14 knots. She carried 2 x 3 inch guns and 8 Lewis guns, had a complement of 55 naval personnel and a small Chinese crew. Whilst there, Jack himself became ill with malaria and not having suitable facilities on board the Captain arranged for him to be transferred to Wuchow where there was a Mission Hospital and a young European doctor. The transfer was done by encasing Jack in a Neil-Robertson Stretcher. When he became convalescent he was invited to watch operations in the hospital and he grew to admire the 26 year old surgeon who tackled operations which in the UK would have been considered as a specialist's province. He was particularly struck with a 7lb sweet jar which the surgeon kept on his office table – it was full of gall and kidney stones which the doctor had recovered during operations.

A sad incident which Jack Fitch also recalls resulted from the death of a young Able Seaman who had just joined the patrol craft from a large County class cruiser. He was unaccustomed to working in such a small craft as a gunboat and while doubling to a particular 'action station' in a practice exercise, he banged his head on one of the low davits supporting a ship's boat. He fell unconscious and the naval surgeon on board the sister gunboard, HMS *Moth*, decided to transfer him ashore to a nursing home in Canton, where a Doctor Lancaster, a six foot ex-Cambridge hockey blue, was in charge. Unfortunately the young man never regained consciousness. A post mortem had to follow before burial could take place and Jack Fitch was asked to assist Doctor Lancaster in this task. The home had no mortuary, nor suitable instruments and what few items the ship's surgery possessed, were loaned for the purpose. With temperatures in the high 90's, the post mortem took place in an old pill box facing Canton. There, over the stretcher with a paraffin pressure lamp giving the necessary illumination and just a few scalpels, forceps and a metacarpal saw, the doctor managed to remove cranial bones and arrive at the diagnosis of cerebal oedema the actual cause of death. Jack remained in the pill-box to supervise the removal of the body by a Chinese undertaker prior the the afternoon funeral which was in truly naval fashion, but despite the invitation to have a few drinks beforehand, which he accepted, he could not bring himself to attend the funeral with the memory of the post mortem so recent.

Before he left the station to return to the UK on the troopship *Lancashire*, there was an inspection of the Ship's Company by the then Commander-in-Chief, China Fleet, Vice Admiral Sir Percy Noble who promised all who had served in such trying conditions of poor accommodation, spasmodic mail and monotonous food, that they would receive the Naval General Service Medal to which was to be added a clasp marked 'WEST RIVER' 1937–38.

This news was welcomed by everyone but to this day, no campaign medal was awarded. What makes this so galling is the fact that the same medal with a clasp 'PALESTINE' 1934–39' was given to anyone in the

Royal Navy who had spent a few days in Haifa during the years of the troubles in Palestine – some actually receiving the award without setting foot in Haifa. In commenting upon this in true philosophical naval fashion, Jack Fitch concluded his report by writing, 'Never mind, I shouldn't have . . . well volunteered – which I did!'.

A PSBA's Haslar Training during the Second World War

By Ex-SBA Eric Alleston

I came to Haslar to make up a class of about 20 HO's all PSBA's in February 1941. Our sleeping quarters were on the top floor of the Staff Quarter's building where we slung hammocks from fittings and we were allowed use of part of the Bar on the ground floor. During air raids, the off duty staff laid hammocks on the ground floor corridors and hoped for a cat-nap. Our combined mess and lecture room was in the block above the main entrance and was heated by an open fire grate which by rota we all took turns to clean and re-fuel. The Medical Officer was a Surgeon Lt. Commander A. E. Gunn and our Sister Tutor, whose name I forget but because she always completed her lectures by mentioning the Alimentary Canal, was nicknamed 'Rectum Rosie'. I passed out as SBA in May 1941, sewed on my Red Cross Badge and was drafted to Al Ward – Acute Surgical, a long 30 bedded ward heated by 2 boxlike coal fire stoves. The ward was cleaned twice daily, beds being moved to the centre of the ward, the deck swept and bumped by heavy Ronuk polishers. VAD's cleaned lockers and when not so engaged, prepared drums of dressings for sterilizing. As a newcomer, I did all the dirty jobs, filling coal buckets, taking dirty dressings to the incinerator and any odd job that was required – a real dog's body, hardwork, sore feet covering miles daily. Later, we were allowed to prepare patients for the Operating Theatre. Heaven help you if you cut a patient with the open razor. A certain Surgeon Commander Williams used to say plenty if it happened and spoke about issuing 'Hurt Certificates' before an operation. He was a feared MO but very highly skilled. I remember him coming to have a look around the ward one evening before dinner and examining a patient who was due for an operation. The MO's jacket was covered in vomit and it appeared that the patient had sneaked some food from the galley. The poor SBA temporarily in charge of the ward at time of the theft, had his week-end leave stopped.

In June 1941, I saw there were 6 vacancies for an X-Ray Training Course and I applied and was interviewed by 3 MO's, two of whom were Surgeon Commander Savage (Radiologist) and the Instructional Medical Officer, Surgeon Lt. Commander Gunn, I was successful, 4 of us were HO's and 2 regulars. The training lasted 3 months and during this period 'M' Block was used as overspill accommodation for SBA's and I applied for a move and got a *bed*!! – no hammock slinging. We had no means of measuring X-Ray dosage other than a monthly blood count but Commander Savage arranged for us to use a balcony in Z Block for sun bathing to counter radiations build up. This was during our free time but a certain Wardmaster Officer had other ideas and he wanted us to do other work but when this reached the ears of the Radiologist, the idea was dropped. Our only text book was a free instruction book issued by Kodak. At the end of 3 months we had a 2 hour written paper; we all passed and were allowed to wear the letter 'X' above our Red Cross Badges, and to receive an extra 3d. (1.25p) daily as an allowance. We were all very special now but we all returned to War Duties, myself to A 11 Officers' Surgical and found myself 2nd I/C to an LSBA, a pre-war male nurse from whom I learned a great deal. Life in the ward was less hectic. I remember a visit made to the ward by Sir William James, the C-in-C, Portsmouth, and his wife one evening. They had come to see their son who had been admitted for removal of his appendix. The Admiral carried his cap under his arm and asked me if it was convenient to see Lieutenant James. The Admiral was a real gentleman. Then in January 1942, I was drafted to Ceylon and did not return to the UK until 1945 when I joined HMS *Gosling*, near Warrington, Lancs, one of the many 'mushroom' Fleet Air Arm Training Establishments. As an LSBA which I had become whilst overseas, I applied and was accepted by the General Nursing Council as a State Enrolled Assistant Nurse but didn't follow it up, returning to my original trade as a decorator, eventually becoming a lecturer until my retirement, at the Salford College of Technology.

During my time in Haslar, I learned a great deal especially from observing doctors and surgeons making a diagnosis and recognised 3 cases of appendicitis whilst serving overseas when no MO was to hand. The X-Ray room at Haslar in my day had 2 machines fed by a line from the Dockyard Power Station. The current to the tubes was fed by overhead bare wires – yet the equipment worked well.

Perhaps the oddest X-Ray I saw was a patient's lower leg in which a wood screw had been used to help repair a fracture. He complained of some pain which an operation cured by tightening the screw – diagnosis – loose screw!!

The Mediterranean in 1942

By ex – LSBA Ron Church

LSBA Ron Church joined the RNH Haslar for his training in November 1940 and was there in 1941 when the hospital's museum and £80,000 of medical stores were destroyed in an air-raid. For days afterwards, he recalls, feathers from stuffed birds, former resplendent museum exhibits, were flying everywhere. Then in the summer of 1941, Ron was drafted to HMS *Nile* in Alexandria and eventually to the naval wing in the adjacent 64th General Hospital. This move involved almost a 12,000 mile trip firstly from UK via the Cape to Durban and Port Tewfik, thence by Egyptian rail to Alexandria. For war time, life there was far more pleasant than in the UK, a lovely climate, good food and adequate shore leave where there were good facilities, for sport and entertainment – but life was soon to alter. In the summer of 1942, he was drafted to HMS *Belvoir*, a Hunt Class Destroyer armed with 4″ guns, 4 barrelled pom-poms and oerlikons. Most of the duties were concerned in protecting convoys plying between Alexandria and Malta which at that time, was almost beleaguered. German air raids on any convoy approaching the island were routine events and many vessels were sunk. One night, in response to a distress signal from HMS *Welshman*, a mine-layer which had been torpedoed, they dashed to the scene only to find that it had sunk and survivors, engulfed in oil fuel were struggling in the sea. Thirty men were rescued by HMS *Belvoir* but many died later through exposure and the ingestion of fuel oil. Everyone heaved a sigh of relief when the *Belvoir* reached the island and the comparative safety of Sliema Creek.

This strain on all ship's companies escorting convoys in the Eastern Mediterranean had its effects on the mental outlooks of some men producing in them a state of apathy. They often appeared dazed for some time afterwards though physically, they were without injury but if their ship had been sunk in the bombing, they would have made no attempt to escape. In reality they were suffering from a kind of 'mental concussion'.

In November 1942, the allied landings in North Africa occurred. Planned as Operation 'Torch' it was carried out under conditions of great secrecy and the enemy was deluded into the assumption initially that a large convoy of shipping was passing through the Mediterranean in yet another attempt to get supplies through to Malta. But when the diversification of the assaults became known, the enemy realised the true objective namely the elimination of all its forces in North Africa.

This was followed by the invasions of Sicily and Italy and with these successes, Malta and the Mediterranean in general became relatively free of enemy aircraft.

Many of Ron's contemporaries were not accustomed to discipline and found naval life very trying but being a scout from boyhood and having an ex-regular soldier as a father, Ron slipped into the routine without undue concern.

Though he has never visited Haslar since his time as a PSBA he has a married daughter who lives in the Isle of Wight and when crossing the Solent to visit her, he looks towards the expanse of the hospital buildings and remembers the days of his training. Like most ex-service personnel who sometimes speak of those awful days, in reality they retain a soft spot for them nevertheless.

From HMHS Maine to the Desert

Incidents in the career of ex-SBA R Sebbage

SBA Sebbage went to sea in the battleship HMS *Resolution*, then he saw service in the Hospital Ship *Maine*. In the mid 30's and during the Second World War he worked in a most unusual capacity in the defence of Tobruk. The following are extracts from the most eventful incidents in his career.

'After completion of my training in RN Hospital, Chatham as a Sick Berth Attendant I was drafted to HMS *Resolution*. I was like a dog with two tails. A battleship above all warships. By gum I was pleased, for battleships, in those prewar days, were the prestige units of any Fleet.

My mate Wilf and two seamen ended up in a six-inch gun casement which was to be our mess – our home. The breech of the gun occupied most of the mess space but we found we could eat our meals from a small table that could be suspended from the deckhead. We soon settled in and began to find our way about this enormous ship. I remember the smell of cooking food, I was always hungry, also the other odours of tarred rope, fuel oil, fresh paint, newly washed underclothes, bread baking in the early morning, disinfectant and scrubbed decks, sweating sailors or the perfume of talcum powder on naked matelots just out of the showers.

As I said, Wilf, my mate was in the same Mess as myself, the six inch casement on the Port side of the ship. This particular gun was manned by a crew of Royal Marines and one forenoon whilst we were exercising with attendant destroyers, the Marines were closed up for gun drill. To their horror, when they opened the breech of their beloved gun, low and behold, there inside were Wilf's toilet gear laid neatly on the metal opening. All hell was let loose and after closing the breech and finishing the drill routine, the Marines went in search of Wilf the culprit. For this heinous offence he was brought before the Commander who had no sense of humour and Wilf was lucky to get off with a hell of a bottle. That week in the Atlantic with the combined Mediterranean and Atlantic Fleets, it was a most wonderful sight. Just imagine it today – sometimes in line ahead as far as one's eyes could see, or in two lines abreast, three mighty Aircraft Carriers, six majestic battleships, thirty fussy destroyers. Then under orders from the Flagship, they would alter course, weave in and out of one another's tracks at full steam or fire ear shattering broadsides.

Every time the *Resolution* fired, clouds of dust came down from the deckheads though we were for everlasting cleaning them, it made me wonder where the dust came from.

My time aboard *Resolution* proved to be brief for after exercises with other units at sea in the Atlantic I was disembarked to HMS *Rooke*, the naval shore base on the Rock of Gibraltar for about two weeks with orders eventually to join the Hospital Ship *Maine*.

Joining her with my kitbag in one hand and my hammock slung over my shoulder I had to report to the Warrant Wardmaster, who was (so I had been told) a very dour Scot, tall, lean and as I was soon to discover, very strict.

I was taken along the upper deck to a sliding door on the Starboard side which opened into a small rectangular Mess running athwartships. It boasted two scuttles, one on either side of the ship. A collapsible scrubbed wooden table was fixed to the deck and it occupied about half the length of the mess and on either side of the table were long benches covered in red rexine. Apart from a bookshelf, two arm chairs, which had seen much better days, and a cupboard in which was kept the milk, sugar, tea and cutlery – that was it. We shared a refrigerator in the Sick Berth Petty Officers' Mess which was next door foreward, a much more inviting compartment which even boasted a carpet and was the home of four Sick Berth PO's and one mighty Sick Berth Chief.

In our Mess there was 'Pricky' Jack, tall, slim and pale but friendly and energetic. 'Wilf' Syer, fair of complexion, muscular and full of bull, 'Nocker' White, who I discovered was an expert footballer and looked every bit an athlete, 'Taff' Lloyd who was quite a serious type and wore glasses, 'Taff' Woodhouse – a real bounder full of flannel and fun, Quigley, a most reclusive chap who somehow was not popular, 'Father' Truscott, a hefty type, older than the rest of us and the Senior Hand in the Mess – a most likeable fellow, he was always skylarking and was a most reliable messmate. Then there was Spencer – a pal of Truscott, the pair always went ashore together and if there was anything going on and whatever was the latest buzz – they knew all about it. There was also 'Tansy' Lee, another friend of Truscott, and lastly 'Sid' Showell. Quite a crowd as you will agree and together we made up the junior nursing staff of His Majesty's Hospital Ship *Maine*.

As a new member of the Mess, I was put through the usual initiation ceremony of being hoisted aloft in a Neil Robertson Stretcher, upside down of course, and there remaining suspended until Spencer and Company decided that I had had enough. Since I was physically fit and showed no undue displeasure, I was quickly accepted into the fraternity.

Below decks our work in the Wards was much the same as the daily routine in any Naval Shore Hospital, except for the steady rise and fall of the vessel as she ploughed on towards Malta which made the use of surgical trolleys an acrobatic act.

There was one main Operating Theatre, a GU Theatre and a Laboratory amidships on the main deck. Aft on the starboard side was the Physio' Department and alongside it the Mortuary. On average there were three operations daily on Patients in the Surgical Ward foreward. They were brought up to the main deck by way of a hand winched cotlift. Attending to a patient on return from the theatre proved impossible since there was no room in the cot-lift for the patient and an SBA.

All the ward cots were slung on gimbals with a tray fixed across from side-to-side which served as the patient's table for his meals etc. Toilets (Heads), Showers and Baths were available at the end of the Wards. The showers and baths were a great luxury since there was always a constant supply of hot water, except of course when the ship was in dry dock.

Food had to be carried from the main galley on aluminium trays, then transferred to plates for serving within the wards – chores which always fell to the most junior Sick Berth Staff (me included) as did all other menial tasks.

The Medical Ward lay aft and above it were the Officers' Wards, Medical and Surgical. The Zymotic Ward was below the ship's waterline.

All Medical Officers had their cabins on the Upper Deck, the Officers of the Royal Fleet Auxiliary Service, who were in charge of the Seamanship of the vessel, had their quarters above, grouped around the Bridge and they were seldom in contact with the likes of us.

The Maltese crew lived at waterline level and we only saw them in the early mornings when they scrubbed the decks and through the day when they manned the liberty boats.

Shortly after joining the ship orders were received to proceed to Gandia on the West Coast of Spain, which at that time (1937) was in the grip of a Civil War and *Maine* had been ordered to embark refugees from Gandia which, when completed, we made out to sea. An hour later shells suddenly began to scream around and about us and it transpired that we were being shelled by the Spanish Cruiser *Balearius*. Our own escort destroyer soon retaliated and the *Balearius* ceased its attention.

We made our way northwards across the Gulf of Lyons in heavy seas and soon the upper deck was crowded with very sick, vomiting refugees.

As I have explained earlier, all our female refugees were from Maternity Hospitals and babies, as ever, seem in a hurry to enter this world and our experience was no exception. It soon became very obvious that our own Doctors would have to make a few deliveries and as far as I now recall, there were four.

This was a new experience for SBAs who are not trained to deal with postnatal problems or any midwifery situations, though on reflection, we should have been.

Babies' cots were made out of fishnets cut from the ship's trawl, toy rattles of the most ingenious designs were improvised, condoms soon found a new use when fitted over the necks of medicine bottles to be used as feeders and many of us became quite adept at entertaining the younger children of refugees.

My first sight of the island of Malta was on a most beautiful summer morning, the Mediterranean sparkled in the sunlight like a million shimmering diamonds, the air was soft, balmy and warm and I was glad to be alive.

We remained there at Pieta Creek during which time my friend Wilf and I explored all the bars in Sliema as well as those of Valleta, and each time we returned to the ship we were very merry to say the least and both of us became known for our insobriety.

Just before Christmas there was a knockout darts competition at Carry's bar in Sliema between the PO's and the Junior Rates. The Seniors were defeated and the victors, whom we all applauded, won the prize – a bottle of whisky. It was, of course, illegal to bring spirits on board ship, hence when one of the victorious team staggered up the gangway, brandishing the prize bottle and shouting 'We've won it you buggers' there was immediate consternation from the Gangway staff. The Duty Petty Officer took charge and put the chap in the rattle or, as it was technically known, for 'being in charge'.

The following day our mess decided to take revenge on the Duty PO for his action, yet the poor unfortunate chap was only doing his duty. All the gilt buttons were removed from his No 1 suit as it hung in his locker, the rest of his clothing was stuffed in his kitbag, which during the night hours was ditched in the 'oggin'.

As might be expected, the following morning all hell was let loose, the whole ship's company was astonished and angry to think that such indiscipline had arisen over such a trifle. Lower Deck was cleared of Juniors, the Warrant Wardmaster harangued us all for our insubordination, our mean despicable actions and total lack of moral understanding. No one admitted to the heinous crime and this meant that we all had to suffer as a group. As Juniors, and the fact that it was a somewhat juvenile prank, we all felt we had been ill-used and were quite prepared to accept collective punishment – so we waited.

Two days passed and nothing happened, then a letter was pinned on the staff notice board which announced that no action would be taken until after Christmas Staff dance, which was to be held at Bighi Royal Naval Hospital – a function we all wished to attend. So meanwhile normal night leave ashore continued.

Bighi Hospital lies on the south side of the Grand Harbour. In a round-about way, it could be reached by road but it was easier to cross the Grand Harbour by boat, usually in a Maltese craft known as a dghaisa. Off we all went to the Christmas Dance, seven of us and we had a whale of a time and in the early hours of the following morning we came down to the jetty to return to the ship. We were just about to leave in our boat when we noticed the Warrant Wardmaster officer all poshed up in his mess dress uniform about to depart in his own boat. 'If you boys want a lift in my boat, jump in' was his greeting – and we lost no time in accepting his offer.

Well the situation turned rather nasty as it was whispered that we should challenge our Wardmaster and threaten to ditch him in the middle of Grand Harbour if he went ahead with a punishment for the 'Whisky' incident. A heated argument ensued, we rocked the boat and the Maltese coxwain took fright, the boat capsized and we all had to swim ashore.

No doubt the swim cooled our alcoholic ardours but the incident had been seen by other warships and we found ourselves arrested by a party of Royal Marines and dripping wet, we were escorted back to HMHS *Maine*. This time our actions received immediate punishment in an official reprimand by the C-in-C Mediterranean and the ship was despatched to Dubrovnik and all our shore leave was stopped for a month.

In these modern times the very thought of having a hospital ship that was coal fired must strike fear in every surgeon. In those days, they never turned a hair, when coal ship time arrived, patients were discharged to their own ships or to shore hospitals. Then all members on board sorted out their old shirts and shorts, had an early breakfast and then turned to unloading the coal lighters that hugged the ship's sides like suckling pigs. It was heavy work humping those heavy coal bags, coal dust penetrating every nook and cranny. Soon everybody appeared like the cast of Show Boat or the Black and White Minstrels, the perspiration running in rivulets down their bodies accumulating in rather delicate places. When the last bag had been taken in a huge sigh of relief was audible throughout the ship. A very late supper was served, black bodies were showered repeatedly and the hammocks provided the solace of sleep – a just reward for the hard work.

As the events of World War II progressed, it became evident that our Maltese anchorage was becoming untenable and orders were received to sail for Egypt, Alexandria to be precise. As we steamed out of Pieta Creek, the ramparts of Valleta were crowded with well-wishers, the bells of St Johns tolling in the distance. No more runs ashore, no more crazy rides in dilapidated gharries singing our way back to the ship in the early hours. Never again would I see the infamous 'Gut' in Valleta where we spent out money on so called sherry for the girls, no more would we guzzle enormous quantities of Stella Beer. The girls would miss us no doubt, so would the barman. It would be the last time the contingents of sailors would 'shoot the rapids'. This meant being seated in a toboggan supplied by whatever Bar was competing and then being dragged by a team of runners down the length of the 'Gut', which I should explain was a lane, bounded on both sides by a series of Pubs of mixed reputations, which descended throughout its whole length by a series of steps. All these memories passed through my mind as we left behind the Island of Malta, often referred to as the Isle of Hell's Bells and Smells. Onward we steamed across the seemingly ever blue Mediterranean for 1500 miles towards the land of the Pharoahs. The nights were calm and the stars gilttered in the dark sky as if they were jewels scattered by the hand of Zeus at the dawn of time.

I became the friend of the local feluccaman who kept three boats close to No 6 Gate, the exit used by all sailors when they went ashore. At first I used to pay him 20 piastres an hour for his services but when he could see that I could handle a boat as well as himself he allowed me complete freedom to use one of his boats unaided. Naval personnel were not allowed to be out of uniform except for sporting activities and I considered that the sailing of a felucca came within this regulation. Thus it occurred that one day when I was to be seen in the felucca wearing a floppy hat and a blue and white striped sweat shirt and looking like one of the natives with my bronzed complexion, I suddenly found myself being hailed by the Quartermaster of the battleship HMS *Warspite*. Thinking I was about to be reprimanded for being improperly dressed, with a fair skill, I brought the craft alongside *Warspite's* gangway.

'Take Captain Crutchley to No 6 Wallah' was the message from the Quartermaster. In got the Captain in full uniform and in constant fear of recognition I ferried him to the shore. How much young man? he queried as he stepped on the jetty. 'Fifty piastres' I replied trying to effect a foreign accent. He gave me the money – no tip and was off. Little did he realise that he had been seen off by a SBA.

19 *Jan* 1941 The following signal was received in the ship: From Commanding Officer Naval Forces, Alexandria 'One Sick Berth Attendant required for duties Western Desert. Destination unknown. Immediate.'

I was given orders to pack my kitbag, an hour later I was sent to HMS *Nile* and then transferred to HMS *Waterhen*, which in the darkness of Alexandria Harbour was preparing for sea. After an air raid at dawn I was disembarked at the jetty at Tobruch – as is the local spelling. The town had fallen to Australian troops under the command of a Major General Mackay. On the morning of the 2nd Jan. Lt Col Hennessy, Australian Cavalry Regiment, entered the fortress of Tobruch and received the surrender from the Italian Commander, Admiral Vietina, along with 2000 officers of the Garrison forces. I learnt later that some 27,000 men surrendered along with 80 odd tanks and 150 vehicles, and that the smoke I could see in the distant skyline was coming from the Italian Cruiser San Georgio which apparently lay beached and burning in the entrance of the harbour.

Captain Poland was the Naval Officer in Charge of Tobruk and it was to his office that I was summoned on the morning after my arrival.

He sat behind an imposing desk, the design of which appeared reminiscent of Spanish Andalusian furniture. 'Ah', he said, 'you've come to top us up with pills Doc? It's splints and bandages you'll need I think. Your duties here are to administer to all members of the Naval Party any medical attention and you are to draw whatever stores are necessary from the Base at Alexandria when those already here need replenishing'.

I was also ordered to establish a Sick Bay in one of the reasonably intact buildings though it proved almost impossible to find one without shell or explosive damage of some sort. In the end one was found in a relatively reasonable state of damage and by dubious means, taking things from here and there, within three weeks it had a semblance of a Naval Sick Bay. Instruments were laid out on a table, which I nicked from a nearby house, also a couple of chairs. Six beds were supplied by the Australians complete with linen and blankets – where they came from I could only imagine but they were lacking in explanation. When I reported that all was ready for inspection, Captain Poland made a visit and he appeared satisfied and offered further help when needed. From then on and in between air-raids, which occurred with monotonous regularity, I catered for the varied minor injuries sustained by sailors and soldiers alike as they laboured incessantly down on the jetty unloading tons and tons of stores. The air-raids, timed with great accuracy at dawn and dusk daily brought their fair share of casualties, many lenghty stitching jobs to lacerated tissues, endless foreign bodies removed from eyes, numerous burns which were all treated with Picric Acid Jelly or Gentian Voilet. Sunburn, 'Gippy' tummy, heat exhaustion – all such conditions found their way to my ground floor flat, as I called it. During my fourth week of residence a near miss blew in my cherished window frames and from then on only mosquito netting was used as I soon learnt the danger of glass. One poor Merchant Navy seaman, who had a bad bout of diarrhoea could not be nursed in bed because of the linen, so I compromised and sat him on my newly constructed lavatory which was well surrounded with pillows. Here, thought I, he could defecate with impunity – or to put it bluntly – to his backside's content – whilst I attended to his dehydration. Unfortunately, during one dusk aerial bombardment, the road outside was torn up and my treasured commode shattered. The unfortunate patient collapsed on the jagged china throne and, after dragging him free, it was necessary to clean him up and put 27 sutures in his backside.

One fine morning, I decided to have a dhoby session, since there was no laundry available of any nature, and I turned out all my crumpled kit on the forecourt at the back of the Navy House. The whole morning I scrubbed away with 'pussers' hard soap and sea water from the harbour, for there was no fresh water available for washing such trivial things as clothes or bedding. By midday it was all hung reasonably refreshed and neat on a makeshift clothes line drying out, but it was not my day for, at dusk, when the enemy planes made their usual visitation, they decided to drop a bomb on Navy House, they missed the house but not my line of washing, all my morning's work was blown to smithereens. Thereafter I was forced to roam around the area clad only in my precious tin-hat and a pair of khaki shorts.

During my time in Tobruk I had been in good health, despite the innumerable privations until my third month in this unusual job, when one morning I awoke with a terrible nausea which was quickly followed by involuntary projectile vomiting. In a few hours I became as yellow as a Chinese coolie and I am told, finally expired with my hand in a hastily dug hole in the sand, semiconscious. An Army Doctor was summoned by one of my up-patients and he decided that I had Weil's Disease caused by a spirochaete. Apparently, the continued bombardment had caused rats to migrate to safer areas during which periods they had urinated on the desert sands, the germs, it was assumed, had probably become airborne and may have been ingested with food. It all sounded reasonable but I felt dreadful and for two weeks was quite ill, though after the first 24 hours I got up again and carried on my nursing duties to injured seamen from ships. I was given some Salvarsen and began to feel better and as far as I recall the Salvarsen had to be mixed with distilled water. My Italian POWs, who had been seconded to the Sick Bay, gave it to me intravenously. All this time I was still running around, clad only in my tin-hat with its Red Cross Badge painted on the front, and my khaki shorts. Captain Poland was always remarking that maybe, one day, he would see me in uniform.

It was then that, while writing some official letters in his office on a certain forenoon which became very hectic, anti-personnel bombs hit the wall of his office and the ceiling collapsed on top of him. They called me into his inner office and after removing heaps of debris. He was unearthed, thankfully only cut and bruised but his uniform was torn to shreds and I could not fail to remind him that soon I hoped to see him in more dignified naval attire. Despite the situation, he knew my implied inference and said 'Sebbage, you're a Scalliwag'.

After many months of occupation at Tobruk the Army Engineers decided to erect a salt water distillery and there was a lot of activity as they laboured at the plant for several weeks. At last it was finished and the news filtered through that fresh water would be available. The German Air Force was based at Derna, just 100 miles up the coast, and since we had no air cover whatsoever, our vulnerability was obvious. This being the case, the enemy took the prime opportunity of sending over a single reconniassance plane to drop a small parachute which bore a message written in English, it stated: 'We shall be over at sunset to remove your newly completed distillery, hope you don't mind'.

Dusk was descending and I stood with the Yeoman in a slit trench in front of the building. Way up the harbour entrance I could still see the dim outline of the half sunken Italian Cruiser *San Gergio*, then suddenly from the mainmast top, a bright light began to shine and flash. The NOIC and his staff were alerted. It soon became obvious that the incoming enemy planes were homing in on this light and in they swooped, one following another in line ahead. In half an hour it was all over and the Distillery was in a shambles.

Daily bombing of the harbour continued throughout April, having a devastating effect on our supply ships. Despite this, over 5000 prisoners were taken to Alexandria by ships of the Inshore Squadron which continually transported men and stores along the North African coastline, a trip which became known as the 'Spud run'. The Hospital Ship *Vita* arrived during this period carrying much needed medical supplies and replacements of medical orderlies for the field outposts. The enemy immediately knew for they sent over a reconnaissance plane which dropped a message in plain English which read: 'Will bomb Hospital Ship if she remains in Harbour'. We did not comply for it was quite legal under the Geneva Convention for the ship to be there. In the early evening over came the Stukas, down screamed the bombs and the *Vita* was severely damaged.

HMS *Waterhen*, the ship that had brought me to Tobruk, took *Vita* in tow out to sea, she also managed to rescue 437 Patients, 6 Doctors, 6 Nursing Sisters and 47 Sick Berth personnel. The previous night *Waterhen* had escorted *Balmaha*, the cargo ship into Tobruk with hundreds of tons of petrol. When *Vita* was seen to be in peril, we at Navy House had sent out lighters to assist in the rescue. A considerable number of Australian Nurses had descended rope ladders slung over the ship's side and I well remember the sight of one Sister who clung desperately to a bottle of whisky which made her descent somewhat difficult, but she would not let go even to the helping hands below. The din was deafening as we ferried the nurses ashore, what with the constant scream of the bombs, the inevitable explosions and the incessant AA fire.

The months passed, Spring gave way to Summer, the guns never ceased their pounding, and the beds in my Sick Bay filled and emptied as the sick and lame were despatched on their way to Alexandria. When would it all end? Funny it's fear and anxiety that teaches you to pray – not preachers or churches. But that statement is a blasphemy, for if it were not for preachers and their churches, I would not have known how to pray. Perhaps I thought, one day I'd go home and roam the English countryside, find a quiet woodland with primroses and bluebells and listen to the Almighty speaking peace to all mankind through the voice of a blackbird.

The siege of Tobruk commenced in April 1941, and Field Marshall Rommel advanced up to the perimeter defences pounding them by night and day. Ships trying to unload suffered very badly and soon the harbour was like a graveyard, masts and spars poked up all over. Whilst carrying a seaman, who had a compound fracture (tib' and fib'), on a stretcher with the assistance of a naval AB, we were blown over by the blast of a bomb and my patient was further injured. I resplinted him in the mouth of a cave and later that night he was sent back to Alexandria by destroyer.

Such incidents were commonplace, dashing up and down the jetty bringing in injured seamen and soldiers who were caught while unloading the backlog of stores. After nine months of heavy bombardment by the Artillery of the Africa Corps and repeated penetrations of our perimeter defences by German armour, the British Army Command gave the order for our evacuation. All arms were mustered, essential stores made ready and installations useful to the enemy were destroyed. Destroyers from Alexandria were to pick up the majority of the soldiers by arriving in relays at the dead of night and the South African Brigade was to cover our retreat. I mustered my medical effects and carried what was possible in a valise slung over my shoulder. My five remaining patients were put on stretchers, the war pattern type, and a party of sailors from Navy House were detailed as stretcher bearers.

With a couple of tots of Navy Rum inside us for good measure, we began to make our precarious way across the rubble strewn road towards the jetty. The rescue destroyers could not reach the inner jetty opposite Navy House and we had to skirt along the coast about half a mile to the oil pipe line which, stretching right out into the middle of the outer harbour, afforded useful protection for our ships. All around the old oil depot lay the wreckage of war and carrying stretchers over the obstacles proved almost impossible but with sweat running off us seemingly in buckets and with much cursing we made it.

The pipeline was still intact, the pipes being about 24 inches in diameter, just sufficient room for us to lay a stretcher, the feet of the stretchers giving enough grip on the side of the pipe to prevent it falling off and into the water. Laboriously we dragged the patients along. At each pipe joint we had to lift the stretchers over the flanges. Twice I remember slipping, almost falling into the water beneath. Those patients who were able to use their hands helped edge themselves along, it was all very exhausting and all the time enemy shells fell unnervingly close, periodically sending up columns of sea water drenching us. Obviously, the enemy knew what we were doing and although it was dark they knew exactly where to aim their shells.

At long last we reached the vague outline of a destroyer and utterly exhausted I clambered over the ship's guardrail. Willing hands reached out, grabbing the stretchers and heaving them onboard. I sank into a fitful sleep just where I lay on the deck. How reassuring it was to wake and hear the pounding of the ship's screws as she made her way to the open sea.

So it was that HMS *Hero* returned us all to Alexandria, where I disembarked, still wearing my tin hat and shorts – by then without boots and I decided to walk into the town and report to the base unit or HMS *Nile* at Raz el Tin.

Maybe I was the only sailor to tramp barefoot and without uniform throughout the streets of Alexandria but not for long because when I arrived in *Nile* they very quickly re-clothed me.

Eventually, I left by train for Suez, then by boat to South Africa.

Who said life as a SBA was dull?

My 22 Years in the Branch

Events in the Career of ex SBPO A. T. H. Rogers who served from January 1937 until pensionable age

I joined the Royal Navy in January 1937, reporting as directed to the RN Barracks, Portsmouth and signed papers to become a Probationary Sick Berth Attendant. There I carried out disciplinary training with others who were to become Cooks, Stewards, Supply Assistants and Waiters. Every morning I was awakened in my hammock by a Duty Petty Officer who came in the mess and gave the first hammock he met a terrific heave, sending the occupant careering into the next, a manoeuvre which was repeated all round the mess deck. After dressing I joined the rest of the class for Physical Training on the Parade Ground. There followed squad drill sessions with rifles and fixed bayonets and during the afternoons, lectures on naval topics. Then began my training at Haslar Hospital where first I was medically examined by the Instructional Medical Officer before joining the Junior class for a 3 month anatomy course. With an examination successfully completed I was then transferred to the Senior Class for instruction in Physiology, Pharmacy, First Aid, Ships Books' forms, Cooking for the Sick and General Nursing. Our Instructional Sister who was nicknamed 'Screaming Skull' was very helpful and I passed my 9 months examination for Sick Berth attendant. I worked on 'Dirty Surgical' for 1 month and had my first experience of lancing an abscess also the first death of a patient who had developed leukaemia. Then in November 1938, I was drafted to Malta and just before I left I married. Taking passage for Malta in the new destroyer HMS *Nubian*, together with other SBAs, life at the RNH Bighi was a little humdrum even though war was declared in September, 1939. Early in the June of 1940, Italy joined Germany in the war and I soon learned the difference. At 0600 the next morning Italian aircraft came over on what was a reconnaissance flight and returned that night dropping bombs on a hilltop monastery. Early in June, whilst on duty in the Surgical block with the Medical Officer and an LSBA, a plane dived on the hospital and dropped a bomb. The LSBA was killed outright, the doctor injured with shrapnel but I seemed to get away with it but I experienced a phenonema and imagined the doors, fittings, electric lights and other fixtures were quietly leaving their moorings and moving slowly towards the opposite wall. A day or so later I was transferred to Imtarfa, the general military hospital inland where I remained until 1942. Whilst working there I saw many casualties and on a certain Friday night when the *Illustrious* was dive bombed whilst approaching the Island, Imtarfa's casualty inmates totalled 250. Everyone worked flat out that weekend, meals were ignored and even up patients turned to by making cups of tea and toast for any of the staff who could take a break. On Easter Sunday Eve, 1941 German aircraft bombed Malta and about 120 HE bombs fell in the hospital area. It was grim but casualties were few considering the scale of the raid. Malta is built on soft rock and buildings are made up of sandstone and they stood up well to the bombing. In 1944, Crete was invaded and it appears the hospital staff there were marched out to form a shield against the Germans as they advanced. We were alerted to this, everyone expecting invasion, but thank God, it never materialised. Air raids continued but we appeared to be left alone, life was a bit cruel for us from June 1940 until the end of November 1941, we had no mail from home, the only news about air raids on Southern England came via BBC broadcasts.

At the end of January 1942 we were relieved by other Sick Berth staff and we joined a merchant ship in a convoy sailing for Alexandria. The Italian Air Force found the convoy and for two days dive bombed us during the daylight hours at 2 hour intervals. We escaped unscathed and duly arrived at Alexandria where we were drafted to HMS *Sphinx*, a naval transit camp just outside the town where we eventually travelled by rail to Cairo, re-training for Port Suez. Trucks then transported us to a POW Camp which was run by the New Zealand Army. They were splendid chaps and produced lots of tinned food and beer which was marvellous after a near starvation diet in Malta. 14 days we spend in this 'paradise' and then embarked in a one funnel Royal Mail steamer for Durban where, on entering the port, we were greeted by the 'White Lady of Durban' who became celebrated for her welcoming songs such as 'Rule Britannia' and 'There'll always be an England' which she sang to all new arrivals of Servicemen.

After a stay in Durban, 120 of us joined the 23,000 ton P and O ship *Empress of Japan* with 1000 women and children all Singapore evacuees destined for England. I was with a party of about 24 Sick Bay men but as the ship's own Sick Bay Complement was adequate, we were given the duties of patrolmen which meant keeping a watch on the passengers and assisting them in any way. Sailors have a way with children and everyone got on with them splendidly. We called in at Capetown where the local population treated us in a lordly fashion, then after a week in the South African sunshine we crossed the South Atlantic, sailed up the coast of South and North America, then via Iceland to the United Kingdom. Being a fast ship, she could outstrip the speed of any U-boat and the first warship we sighted was off the coast of Northern Ireland. Many thought it was a German ship until a message over the ship's broadcast informed us it was British. Finally we docked in Liverpool, then via rail at Lime Street to London and late one night we arrived at Portsmouth Town Station, hardly believing our luck. The next day we were all granted Foreign Service Leave from Portsmouth Barracks. Getting on the top deck of a bus to Fareham, I saw 'barrage' balloons above certain places in the dockyard and immediately asked other passengers what they were. I think they thought me quite mad but when I explained I had never seen them before they became very friendly. My small daughter, 3 years old who I saw for the first time during my leave, would have nothing to do with me at first and frequently questioned my wife 'Mummy, who is this man?' Sailors today speak of being away for long periods, when they have been at sea for 6 months, I do not know what they would do if they had served on long commissions as in early years. Commissions sometimes lasted 4 and 5 years in fact my father went away to the Cape Station in 1913 before I was born and did not return until 1918 after the First World War.

After leave I was drafted to the RNH Haslar and the reader might like to know what Haslar was like during the war. A bomb had hit the Museum which was situated between C and D blocks, the ground had been cleared allowing ambulances easier access to C ward. The cellars were widely used for patients' sleeping areas, most departments were below ground level including an operating theatre. Haslar was a casualty clearing hospital, cases being transferred to Winchester, Park Prewett, Basingstoke, and other auxiliary hospitals. After a spell working in the dispensary, I went to the Medical School, then at Clevedon, Somerset to take a Laboratory Course and being successful I returned to Haslar and was promoted Sick Berth Petty Officer. As duty PO in the hospital you have a lot of responsibility being in charge of about 4 Leading Hands and 12 SBAs. One night a woman was brought in by the Regulating Staff with a damaged hand which she had pushed through a window. It required suturing and this was done by the Duty Medical Officer in the Receiving Room. When this was completed she was given a note to take to her own doctor but despite my reasoning with her, she refused to leave the hospital and lay on the floor, kicking and screaming. I sent for the Regulating Branch who then informed me that she was a well known local character called 'Scotch Nance' a frequenter of the local pubs. She still would not leave and in the end, the Civilian police were called.

They gave her a cell in the local police HQ where she spent the night, before being released the next day with a fine. The same morning I received a phone call from a man who said he was a friend of 'Scotch Nance' and I had 'done her in' and he would 'get me'. The Commissioned

Wardmaster thought it was just a joke by someone but I was very apprehensive that night as I made my way home. The next day, another phone call was received at Haslar by me and a man's voice asked me to meet him in a certain pub at the lunchtime. I agreed, only to find 'Scotch Nance' sitting in a corner with a non-alcoholic drink. She spoke in a most cultured voice, behaved charmingly and apologised most profusely for her earlier behaviour. Over a drink we parted company amicably. A few months later, I learned she had been forcefully escorted out of the area as a vagrant and prostitute. After a spell in Haslar I was drafted to Singapore and for the later part of the commission I worked at the naval base in the laboratory. Returning home I served some months at the Physiological Laboratory under Doctor Wright, the Scientific Officer who designed the Water Tower in HMS Dolphin and who was an expert in Under Water Medicine. When in 1955 I was drafted to HMS Daedalus to act as Health Inspector and Secretary to the Medical Officer of Health for Air Stations in the course of which I visited all naval stations in turn. Towards the end of my career I returned to Haslar where I had various jobs, in Reception, Outpatients and taking charge of the hospitals equipment. Meanwhile my hearing had becomee steadily poorer and I was eventually invalided from the Service. I have always found that any Senior Medical Officer who was a disciplinarian was a far better officer to work under than one of the 'Hail fellow, well met type' who would often let you down by not standing by you when you were only trying to carry out orders. In fact I got on well with Senior Medical Officers who in the opinions of most sick berth men, no one could work with harmoniously. Perhaps I may have been considered a crank but I owe Hasler so much, on two occasions at least, for saving my life – so I shall always say God Bless RNH HASLAR and may he bless all who serve in her.

Brief Details of SB Training at Barrow Gurney

Commissioned Wardmaster RN (Retd) A. H. Weeks DSM

Mr Weeks very kindly supplied names of the Training Staff who were employed at the RN Auxillary Hospital at Barrow Gurney, near Bristol in 1942. He mentioned that the officer selected for the Training project was the late W. G. (Bill) Blight, then a Warrant Wardmaster who was allowed to select his own Training Staff, viz

　1 SBCPO　　　　　　　(Chatham Division)
　1 SBCPO and 1 SBPO (Portsmouth Division)
　1 SBCPO and 1 SBPO (Devonport Division)
and 2 LSBAs from Devonport Division for office duties.

The Instructional Medical Officer, a Surgeon Commander, Elliot and a Laboratory Specialist who were both in the Training Wing were additionally on the Hospital Staff. Mr Weeks stated that the site of the Training Section was in the Hospital's grounds – entirely divorced from the main hospital and consisted of newly erected Nissen Huts built on heavy clay ground which provided very spartan living conditions. The standard of PSBAs received at Barrow Gurney was described as 'Mediocre' though some of the older men and younger ones who had requested to become Sick Berth Staff was very good; the remainder were 'run of the mill', conscripted men who were not particularly interested in becoming SBAs.

Mr Weeks finished his account of the Barrow Gurney War time training by listing the names of the SB Senior Training Staff who instructed the recruits, these were:

SBCPO H. E. M. JONES	(PORTSMOUTH)
SBPO WOOLY	(PORTSMOUTH)
SBCPO A. H. WEEKS	(DEVONPORT)
SBPO C. GEORGE	(DEVONPORT)
SBCPO 'ALEC' ALLSOP	(CHATHAM)

Stonehouse in 1942

Jottings from ex SBA A. J. E. McCreedy

I arrived at RNH Stonehouse with 12 others in September 1942 to be met by a man who from that day to the day we finished training controlled our every minute. There he stood, four square, a portly figure in a number 1 suit complete with gold badges a 3 Badge PO. What a man, he didn't talk, he stalked: He looked like the *Victory* in full sail. We got to know him well as we had to wait 3 weeks for enough men to form a new class and during that time we PSBAs, the lowest forms of life in the RN, did everything from scraping the polish off wooden floors and then repolishing them to emptying a basement storeroom of hammocks that had been there since Drake played bowls. Another person I well remember was the Sister Tutor, the fastest bed-maker I have ever seen. When I make a bed at home, which is not often I can still hear her voice and I make the corners square and the sheets tight. How she managed to make us into SBAs and to keep her sense of humour is beyond me. She told us how to raise the end of a bed, to lie the patient on his face with a receptacle handy so that he could clear phlegm from his lungs. Turning to one of the class she asked him to repeat what she had said which he did but added that to get rid of any phlegm, he would slap him on the back and grab his ankles so that he would not slide out of bed. The class including Sister just exploded with laughter.

I could never understand the duty I was given during the many air raids on Plymouth. When the siren sounded I had to dash to my Passive Defence Station which was at the top of the clock tower. I ran like hell to this place almost collapsing when I got there until I got my breath back. Then I had to pick up a phone and when a voice at the other end said 'Hello', I had to reply 'RNH' and then ring off. My instructions were to remain in the post throughout the raid while the tower shook with bombs exploding and AA guns firing all round. Then the 'All Clear' would sound but I had to remain there until the phone rang when the voice said 'Carry On'. It was just after we passed out as SBAs that the class had a lucky break. By then we had a new job during the air raids, we manned a ward ready to deal with casualties. On one night when we were duty watch and ready to turn in, we heard planes overhead, then the sound of bombs falling and exploding in the hospital grounds. As that occurred, the sirens sounded and we dashed off to the ward. I remember the glass we crushed under our feet as we ran but it was not until daylight that we saw the damage and realised that if the sirens had sounded first, we would have run into the blast and there is no doubt that most of us would have been killed. The bombs had landed in open spaces but with the earth being so soft, they had exploded on the rocks below and the blast effect was bad. The direction we had taken had been well plastered, walls were embedded with pieces of glass like daggers. It was a very shaky group that surveyed the scene and realised what an escape they had. Later I was moved to the RNAH Sherborne, a marvellous hospital with a great team of Doctors, SB Staff, VADs and WRNS, the whole hospital took its lead from the SRA who was never too busy to talk to you and make you feel glad to be one of his team.

On the Haslar Pas Boat to Portsmouth

Confession of ex POMA K. A. Brown

The following is an extract from a letter received from the above named ex Petty Officer Medical Assistant.

As a newly qualified Medical Assistant in the early seventies, I was drafted to my first Sick Bay at the shore establishment, HMS *Warrior*, at Northwood, Middlesex. On a bright sunny summer morning, resplendent in my full uniform and wearing my newly acquired red cross on my right arm, I stepped on to the PAS boat at Haslar pontoon, to take me the short distance to the Portsmouth Harbour pontoon. As I stood on the upper deck of the boat, with my pusser's suitcase and my kit bag on the deck between my feet, I looked and felt every bit the jolly jack tar. We passed Gosport ferry, loaded with summer tourists and pretty girls and everybody seemed to be waving to me. I waved back as the PAS boat neared the pontoon. Now the Gosport ferry docks on one side of the pontoon and the PAS Boat on the other. As my boat got to within 12 feet of the pontoon I decided to give the tourists a display of naval strength. I picked up my kit bag and heaved it towards the jetty. Very impressive I thought. It hit the side of the pontoon and plopped into the harbour. Fortunately the deck hand on the PAS boat had seen my mistake and fended us off so I could retrieve my kit bag. As I bent over to lift it out of the water I knocked my suitcase in. By now the holidaymakers on the ferry were doubled up in fits of laughter. It was a very humble and red faced young MA that had to walk with them towards the station, dirty green seawater dripping from suitcase and kit bag.

That excursion into Portsmouth Harbour cost me dearly – all my spare uniforms and my civies were ruined.

Hurricane David

By CPOMA J. J. Knowles BEM

CPOMA John Knowles in September 1979 was serving in HMS *Fife* when the ship was diverted to Dominica. The northernmost island of the Windward group which, at that time, was in the direct path of a hurricane named 'David', bringing winds in excess of 200 knots. As a result of his experiences in bringing help to the islanders, he was ordered to write a detailed report of events. The document covered 14 pages of single spaced typescript and involved some 10,000 words which if reproduced here would require a whole chapter. The following shortened account it is hoped will give the reader some idea of the most varied duties which a member of the branch may be expected to undertake.

HMS *Fife* visited the West Indies in the July of 1979 and was returning to the UK when news of hurricane David reached the ship which was then ordered to alter course for Barbados which appeared to be in the path of the hurricane. En route the ship's company prepared for the contingency. Stores of every description were unearthed and in the medical sphere these included drugs, surgical instruments and even a portable oxygen unit – in fact any item which might be of use in the treatment of casualties. During the course of these feverish activities a radio news flash revealed that the path of the hurricane had veered towards Dominica, an island some 35 miles long and about 12 miles wide; in consequence the ship's course was altered.

Just before radio stations on the island were silenced by the hurricane's devastation, a late broadcast gave the information that 6 people had been killed and that about 60,000 had been made homeless and the whole island was in a state of chaos.

Arriving off Dominica and viewing it from a range of 2 miles, the situation appeared formidable – the shanty like wooden buildings had been flattened. Not being able to go alongside, the ship's helicopter left with the *Fife's* Commander to seek out the Island's Prime Minister and to enquire what assistance was required. The ship's second helicopter then left with the Surgeon who was keen to liaise with the local Medical officer. Everywhere buildings were in ruins, jagged glass and twisted metal girders were all that remained, in fact it was remarkable from the damage to property that so few people were killed. The ship's surgeon having made contacts on shore and carried out a reconnaissance of the island decided that a 'Field Hospital' should be established in the most devastated village which happened to be situated in a mountainous area. It was to this spot that John Knowles and his staff of 'First Aiders' together with the medical stores were dropped in repeated trips by helicopter. A 'Field Hospital' was set up in the only part of a school which was left standing – the kitchen but in common with every part of the island, it had neither water nor electric supplies. The locals, seeing that all the party wore Red Crosses on their shirts, assumed that all members were doctors and they clamoured around for attention. Apart from on the spot casualties such as flesh torn from limbs, crushed arms, fractured skulls, back injuries and eye infections, there was the ever increasing evidence of other casualties in outlying areas, news of which was given to the team by villagers from neighbouring places. Eventually, members did visit some of the places treating people in most need and assuring others that more medical assistance was on the way. People were so shocked that they walked around in a dazed fashion not knowing where to go or what to do. Most of their injuries appeared to have been caused by flying corrugated iron roofing which had formed the coverings of almost all the island's buildings. The hurricane had lifted these and cut them through like a giant scythe. Not a branch remained on any tree but there was plenty of food available as coconuts, mangoes and bananas were scattered around in profusion. A firm hand had to be taken with the islanders many of whom were inclined to take more notice of the village headman until a naval discipline was enforced. In particular this was essential because of the general, lackadaisical attitude towards elementary hygiene shown by villagers.

Unless a firm hand was taken, they were inclined to ignore the dozens of dead animals which lay rotting away – cattle, horses, dogs and cats, rather than arrange for the carcases to be either burnt or buried. In the interests of hygiene the naval team organised them into burial parties despite the protestations of headmen who were quite content to leave the carcases unburied and suffer the dreadful smell of rotting flesh.

Gradually and with the assistance of the local medical authority some semblance of order took shape and more medical supplies were received from Barbados via HMS *Fife* which had made a trip there to embark supplies which had been air-freighted from the UK by the RAF. After a week working 'in the field' moving by helicopter from village to village, the French Army with a fleet of Gazelle helicopters arrived on the island to establish tented field hospitals throughout. The *Fife's* work was then complete and from the experience many lessons were learned to combat future contingencies. Reports were made as to the right quantities of emergency stores to be carried in warships and what 'First aiders' should be taught to deal with such eventualities.

Full account of events were given in John Knowle's report and for his ingenuity and outstanding contribution in the relief of Dominica, most deservedly, he was awarded the British Empire Medal.

Barnoldswick's Contribution in Two World Wars

Where's Barnoldswick? This is the first reaction by most people when they hear of the name but not so Mrs Shirley Haigh, who was born there and now lives in Skipton, North Yorkshire, often referred to as the Gateway to the Yorkshire Dales. The smaller township of Barnoldswick lies about 8 miles to the south-west and is nearly the same distance from the Lancashire town of Colne further south. From the township a number of young men joined the St John Ambulance Brigade and at the outbreak of the First World War, as a body, they joined the Sick Berth Branch and were drafted to the Hospital Ship *Rohilla*.

Almost two months to the day later, the ship was lost at Saltwick Nab off the Yorkshire coast near Whitby where many of the dead were buried. The story behind the loss of the vessel was published by the firm of Carr Print of Barnoldswick and a plaque commemorating the dead was erected in the former Royal Naval Hospital, Chatham.

The support this small township continued to give to St John Ambulance Brigade and the Sick Berth Branch became traditional for yet another body of men joined the branch in September 1939. Mrs Haigh states that many of them are now dead but she is aware of the two who are still living (ie in November 1983) a Norman Windle, now a retired Insurance Agent and Maurice Myers, who is the local Secretary of the British Legion Branch. In recent correspondence, Mrs Haigh queries whether any other small township has such an unusual connection with the Sick Berth Branch. If anyone knows of such an association perhaps he or she will kindly inform the Curator of the Medical Museum at Haslar. Why should Mrs Haigh be particularly interested? The answer is simple, she was one of the few Wren SBA's in the RN, having joined at Chatham in 1949.

The Sinking of HMS Sheffield

POMA G. A. Meager

On May 4, 1982 HMS *Sheffield* was engaged in the air defence of the South Atlantic Task Group when she was hit amidships by an Exocet missile which caused major damage and casualties. After 4½ hours, with fighting capabilities destroyed and fire approaching the forward missile and gun magazines, the order to abandon ship was given to prevent further loss of life. POMA Meager gave immediate first aid treatment to the more serious casualties, then collecting together his first aid teams, established a most effective casualty centre in the hanger. He provided excellent direction and considerate encouragement where it was needed, comforted those who were suffering from shock and organised the evacuation of casualties by helicopter. At one point, receiving a report that a man below decks had been overcome by smoke, Meager donned breathing apparatus and rescued an unconscious man in most difficult circumstances. He also retrieved the body of another apparently unconscious man to an area where he could attempt resuscitation, though his subsequent determined efforts to save this man's life were unsuccessful.

Later, at the order of abandon ship, he supervised most efficiently the evacuation of the remaining wounded and continued his care for them whilst on board the rescue ship. POMA Meager's selfless dedication to duty and professionalism in difficult circumstances undoubtedly saved life and minimised many injuries.

This is POMA Meager's personal record of events of board HMS *Sheffield*.

'Our First Lieutenant set about preparing the ship for war. Something which until the day we were hit I don't think ever really sunk in. He did this in three stages, so that by the time we left Ascension Islands we were fully prepared and ready for any eventuality, which as it turned out was not wasted. I cannot remember now everything we did in each different stage but I will do my best. First of all as a ship, then as a Medical Department.

The first stages within the ship were mainly to do with stores and ensuring that we had enough of everything to go on with. All equipment was checked and re-checked and demands were made so that we should receive the stores when we got to Ascension. Every piece of loose equipment had either to be removed and placed in a safe stowage or fully secured.

If it couldn't be secured or stowed properly then it was ditched. The ship was painted grey which sounds daft but it's surprising just how many different colours there are on the outside of a warship. By the time we had finished there wasn't anything on the upper decks of

Sheffield that wasn't painted grey. The ship was checked out for darkening ship, there was to be nothing visible to anyone that there was a warship present. Even though we knew there wouldn't be any fighting everybody got on with their tasks with a purpose and there were few moans and groans.

Medically speaking we checked all our equipment. All equipment was still coated in plastic, coatings were removed, cleaned and sterilised ready for instant use. More stores were placed in every conceivable space. Infusion equipment was grouped together with our individual preference of canulas, giving sets and various fluids for every eventuality.

In the second stage I cannot remember much of what went on around the ship. However, everyone on board was given first aid lectures on the basic principles, and they were very basic. My way of thinking was that if a man was dead, then he was either dragged out to a position where he might be given Artificial Respiration and Cardiac Massage or he would be left where he fell, which in the cold light of day sounds callous, but in reality when there are fires, smoke and fumes all around there is no time for the niceties of life. None of us really knew what it would be like and I never heard anybody on board say that they weren't frightened sometime or another. The "Buffer"* gave everybody a very comprehensive lecture on abandoning ship and survival drills. We were issued with once only suits and told how to use them. Medically we gave everyone lectures on hypothermia, frost bite and trench foot. This made a change from telling them what type of Venereal Disease they are likely to catch. Remembering that the "Argies" were going to turn and run when they saw the great British Fleet coming over the horizon, we were certain that no shots would be fired at us. But everyone on board was issued with their Geneva Convention Identity Cards. New lists of blood donors were drawn up and placed around the ship, in every First Aid post and Sick Bay. Everyone was brought up to date with their tetanus, even the over 35's had it whether or not it was needed they got it. If they didn't come to me then I jabbed them where they stood whether it was at work or propping up their bar.

A list of people allergic to penicillin was drawn up and placed with the blood donors' list. The first aid teams were constantly being practised and lectured. Morale was still very high, I think the news that the task force from the UK had sailed and we were not going to take on the "Argies" alone helped. We were very worried about our families because we hadn't been able to notify them of our situation and mail would not have reached home. We were not allowed to telegram them either. Our worry very soon turned to rage when we found out that other ships in our group had telegraphed their families seeing as how we had been

---

* 'Buffer' — the Nickname for the Chief Petty Officer. Boatswain's Mate who passes Orders to ratings and thus acts as the 'buffer' between officers and ratings

away so long and we were due home soon, we were really mad. We were told that the Captain was equally as mad and I have no doubt he was. If there was any change in any situation he would make a pipe and tell us the score. He kept us very well informed the whole time. The "Jimmy" made a 'pipe' every night telling us what was going on and how far the ship had gone in its preparations and what the other ships were doing. Every World news broadcast was listened to no matter how bad the reception. The ship went silent every hour on the hour, in the hope that the diplomats would work out a solution to all and we could go home. As time went on hope for that faded fast.

Our second stage of preparations were completed by the time we got to Ascension Islands. When we got there all our war stores were waiting for us, along with lots of mail, which was a welcoming sight although it saddened us, especially when we found out how our families had been informed of our non-arrival.

The various feelings around the ship were funny, some of the lads were really excited at the prospect of going to war, the other lads were more subdued understandably. Everyone was frightened although no one showed it and I didn't have anyone crack-up at all. But there again there would be no fighting, would there? We would create a loud noise and then the Government would forget it and we would go home five or six months late, but that's life in a blue suit isn't it?

The Commanding Officer of our Destroyer Squadron Captain D3 was on board during the first part of our voyage and gave us some useful and informative information on the Falkland Islands, after all most of the ships company had either never heard of them or if they had, thought they were a group of islands off the coast of Scotland, not 3000 miles away. Ah well what was a few thousand miles between friends?

After all we'd just been halfway round the world and the other half wouldn't make much difference.

Then the bad news came through that we had been chosen, along with a couple of other ships, to go on ahead of the main task group down south. Our third stage of preparation was then put into action. All carpets on Two Deck and below were to be removed and stowed or ditched. All loose furnishings were to be fully secured, all pictures removed from the bulkheads. The only things we were allowed in our lockers were a number one suit, changes of underwear and socks, and some warm clothing in case we had to abandon ship. Everything else had to be stowed in the various store rooms around the ship.

AGRE life jackets and once only suits were everywhere and they were always at hand. All personal photographs were to be stowed away although very few of us went to this extreme. All mirrors were either removed or fully taped up. Defence watches were worked up to a fully organised state as was action messing. The war stores were used where possible to over stock all first aid boxes which had all been previously checked along with the Neil Robertson stretchers. First Aid posts were filled to the brim with every spare piece of equipment that we thought would be useful. The first aid parties were trained in setting up intra venous fluids, giving morphine, penicillin and tetanus injections. I had deliberately left this training to the last in the hope that most of the information would stick in their minds, especially as we were going so close to the Falklands and there was now a very remote possibility that there would be fighting. I drew the morphine from the Captain and distributed it throughout the ship as I saw fit, discussing it with the doctor, First Lieutenant and Captain. We had ten vials on the bridge and 10 in the hanger. The bridge ampules were kept under lock and key in the first aid box, all officers of the watches were briefed on their use. The hanger morphine was under the same lock and key in the hanger first aid box under the care of the Senior Medical Rating, who again was fully briefed. The pilot and observer were also trained in its use. Ten ampules went forward and aft in each first aid post and each of the two team leaders had ten ampules. Ten ampules went in the emergency first aid post which was the Chief Petty Officers' Mess and I had ten ampules together with the doctor. The rest remained in the Sick Bay. The glass ampules were split between the forward First Aid Post, which was also the Emergency Operating Station and the Sick Bay. I did not believe in first aiders and officers walking around with this highly dangerous drug round their necks, especially the officers who hadn't even bothered to come to any of the first aid lectures. Apart from the pilot, observer and the First Lieutenant, none of the other officers were trained in first aid to my knowledge. This is not for want of trying but the usual thing is that an officer will never be in any position to render first aid to anyone. I always get the impression that it's a bit below them but then, as now, they did just the same as many of us did.

The ship was now in full defence watches and fully ready for war. I forgot to mention that all wooden parts of the ship on the upper decks had been removed and that included the air-conditioning doors. Morale was still very high, although the fear in the men was more noticable. Throughout the whole voyage down everyone did what they could to find out just what the "Argies" had and what damage they could do to the ship, how many they would kill if a hit was made in a certain place, whether we could survive an Exocet attack. I know more about Exocet and bombs now than ever I did before and that's not taking into account that we were hit by one. Everyone was the same, we were all frightened of the Exocet, but we thought that because we were an air defence ship and would be used to protect the carriers, we would not be put up against other ships unless the situation got desperate, because we believed that a ship launched Exocet out-ranged our Sea Dart although we had locked on to another ship nearly fifty miles away which was quite astounding, especially because we had no airborne assistance at the time.

May 1st came and we entered the Total Exclusion Zone, sending in a Vulcan bomber to destroy the airfield and Harriers to finish the job. The Vulcan raids, apart from being a bit of a morale booster, were a waste of time but the Harriers appeared to do a great job, having the "Argies" complain that our cluster bombs were inhuman. Where did they get the idea that war was all good fun and no one was to be killed? We experienced our first real action stations that day, we all closed up but it still didn't seem real. They would be so daft as to attack us, we could shoot anything down that they could dish up. Then those terrible words, "There is an air attack mounted, our Combat Air patrol has gone to intercept". We heard that we had shot down a Mirage then the dreaded words that everyone hoped they would never hear, "Take cover an aircraft has fired an "Exocet".' What they didn't tell us that it was 100 miles away, so we all found some sort of a place to hide and proceeded to find out that adrenline was brown, especially when it runs down your legs. We remained where we were for what seemed an eternity, eventually I discussed the prospect of the thing having either reached us by now or not with my team leader and we decided that it was safe to sit up although one of our chefs disagreed for a couple of minutes and stayed where he was. He was to die later.

We were at action stations for most of that day but never fired a shot or saw an Argentine plane, except on a radar screen. By the end of the day we had shot down one Mirage and one Canberra and the "Argies" had shot down two Mirages and abandoned a Canberra although only one of these was officially confirmed. Some of the ships which were doing NGS had been straffed with one of the Type 21's taking a casualty. Still no serious damage done to us and the "Argies" knew for sure that we were here now and meant business. But for us all it still didn't seem real. This may seem strange in the light of what was happening at the time but the fleet felt the same. Unless you have been in that position it's very difficult to explain. Morale was extremely high. The days went on and the air attacks became less and less and so did the action stations.

One night when I was on watch and 'loafing' in the operating room we heard that one of our helicopters had been straffed whilst on its way back to mother, two Lynx were dispatched and one of them attacked a target firing the new air launched missiles. A large explosion was reported but no debris was seen nor were there any survivors in the water but the explosion was certainly a very large one. The second helicopter was fired on and attacked a second target. Again it is thought they scored a hit but no trace of these enemy vessels were found or reported as being lost by the "Argies". What they were remains specu-lation, some think it was a corvette, others that they were armed fishing vessels, we will never know.

During the days that followed life became quite routine on board, action stations were few and far between because we were either out of range or it was a Sunday and of course everyone knows that the "Argies" have to have Sunday off.

The day we were hit started out like any normal day. We were at defence stations and I had been on watch during the morning. The previous night we heard the news flash that the Argentinian Cruiser *General Belgrano* had been torpedoed and sunk with all hands. Although we were immensely happy at the thought of one of their major war ships being sunk the loss of life was very saddening. They were sailors just like us and I think I am right in saying that their loss saddened us all.

At about 1400 I was asleep in my bunk, I woke up looked at my watch and decided that I had another hour in bed before I had to get up for my watch at 1600. A pipe was made "AWO Ops Room AWO", with a sense of emergency, this was followed by a loud crump and the ship shuddered violently. Realising we had been hit by something I fell out of bed, landing on a fellow comrade who was to die later that afternoon. We got our boots on picked up our gear and went off to our action stations. When I got to the Sick Bay I found my doctor slightly dazed with shock but OK, the Sick Bay door was inside the bay (the door opens outwards on a Type 42), a pillow was embedded in the formica behind the doctor's chair and the operating table was slightly buckled. An Engineering Mechanic came into the Bay looking like a gollywog, his hair had been badly scorched and his face, arms and hands severely burned. The burns to his face and arms were superficial but his hands were full thickness where he had tried to climb the starboard ladders from one of the engine rooms. We gave him intravenous pethidine and started to dress his wounds when two other casualties arrived, both Chief Petty Officers, one was suffering from shock and the other had a four inch laceration to his head and shock. I laid the shocked casualty down to rest and proceeded to clean and shave the head injury for dressing it ready to be sutured once we had any fires under control. By the time I had done this a message was passed that helicopters were coming in to take off our casualties, I thought they would be treated quickly once onboard a safe ship so decided to evacuate the three I had. I knew that there was a further casualty in the hanger and intended to evacuate him as well. At this time I still did not know what had hit us, the two Chiefs described their mess as "exploding all around them" which led me to believe that we had been hit by small air launched missiles hitting the Chiefs' mess and one engine room. When I got to the hanger there was a certain amount of confusion, there was little smoke inside the after end of the ship at this time. With the amount of activity going on around the Sick Bay and the after section I knew that it was possible to use the after Petty Officer's heads as a First Aid post so I therefore instructed my Petty Officer writer to set up a post with whatever First Aiders he could find with the First Aid boxes in the hanger and torpedo magazine. This we managed to do, the casualties could not be evacuated by the helicopter aft because our own helo' was still on deck just taking off. (I found out later that it was 45 minutes from go to this point). I was then shouted for to go to the foc'sle as there was casualties forward. This I did, meeting a couple of very distressed senior rates along the way. They had seen the casualties and were horrified at what they saw, I briefly managed to reassure them and carried on. The sight that next hit me is one I will never forget as long as I live. The whole of the port waist was covered with junior rates fighting the fire with buckets of water on lengths of rope so as to cool the superstructure. I made my way forward to the flight deck where I found the worst of our casualties, one Chief Petty Officer with 60 per cent burns and shrapnel wounds, obviously in terrible pain but amazingly he still had his sense of humour. The burns extended over most of his back, the whole of his face, both hands and arms and parts of his legs, the shrapnel wounds were in his buttocks and right arm. He lost completely a small part of the muscle in the arm. We dressed him as best as possible and gave him morhpine, wrapped him up and got him ready for 'casevac'. Another lad had burns to his face and hands, again he was dressed, given morphine and made ready for transfer.

There were two Petty Officers, one with concussion who believed he was the only man left alive, with blood leaking from his left ear, and the other man had burns to his face with small fragments of shrapnel in both eyes and right cheek. Two stewards, one with a head injury and shock and the other severely shocked; a Chief with severe shock so bad that he was rigid, I found out later that he had seen one of the men trapped in a door with his leg amputated and the door trapping him. He died of smoke inhalation and loss of blood though which got him first who knows? We do know that several attempts were made to free him but the door was too badly buckled.

After hearing that the casualties on the forecastle were all dealt with and made ready for evacuation detailing the most serious ones first, I set about establishing a first aid post on the forecastle. It was obvious now that the ship had been hit by an Exocet missile and was badly damaged. I haven't described the smoke and fumes yet but will do so later. I took a Leading Writer with me and went back to the after end of the ship checking at the first aid post who were dealing with a couple of slightly injured casualties and then going into the ship to get out what equipment I thought would be useful.

I managed to get a rescusitator, more morphine and the large First Aid box from the after first aid post. I gave the resuscitator to the hanger party and some of the morphine, then took the rest of the equipment forward and established a post there. We started to see some smoke inhalation and some more shock cases coming through which could be dealt with quite easily because the worst of the other casualties had been evacuated in a Sea King helicopter. Thinking that Sea Kings came from

Hermes or *Invincible* I believed that was where my casualties had gone. I went back aft into the Bay again to get blankets and warm clothing also to take the resuscitator forward where I needed it most. I had only the small oxygen bottle in the kit and a spare I got from the Sick Bay.

A surgical support team arrived from *Hermes* consisting of two doctors but as we had already treated most of our casualties they left as quickly as they came. I then went aft again to check on their progress and to see if they wanted any help but they had everything under control. When I reached the forecastle again all our casualties had gone and I then started to make out a list of casualties and tried to find some idea of the men who were missing. I accounted for 28 casualties and three missing and tried to tell the Captain. One of the ships that had come to our aid radioed him and told him they were going to attack a subsurface contact, I looked up and saw a white torpedo track heading across our starboard beam about fifty yards ahead of us. I've seen enough John Wayne movies to know a track like that when I see one, but surprisingly enough it didn't affect me until much later. After passing on my information I went back to my Petty Officer Steward who was in charge of my party to have a 'fag'. Then a young lad came out of an escape hatch on the forecastle side and stated there were two people trapped by smoke down below. There were a number of BA sets loafing on the deck so I put one on, attached a lifeline to myself and went into the ship leaving instructions with my Petty Officer Steward that when he found out how much air I had left and knew I was running short to give me three tugs on the line. Neither of us could remember how to read the ampimeters so that was the best system. When I look back it was probably the stupidest thing anybody could do but you don't think in those situations, all you know is someone needs help and that is what we are trained for. When I got to the bottom of the vertical ladder it was very difficult to see anything, the smoke was really thick. I should have realised this before I went in because we had just resuscitated three people, one needed full EAR, the other two required oxygen. Still I started to make my way forward where I found a body lying on the deck, he was frothing at the mouth and twitching violently, I dragged him to the ladder and tried to carry him up but I got as far as the third or fourth rung and fell down so I attached my lifeline to him and the lads pulled him out. When I got to the forward section base I saw a glimmer of orange light, I know that one of our PO's had his life jacket on and realised it was him (this was the man I had fallen on top of when getting out of bed), I tried to find whether there was any signs of life but couldn't find any. Calming myself and trying to practise what I'd preached for God knows how long I tried to take my mask and give him a little air in the faint hope that there was still some life in him. I never got the mask off my face before the fumes hit me so I started to drag him out. I got as far as the laundry door and I was breathing very heavily and I was crying with fear and strain. No matter how this reads believe me I have never been so scared of dying in all my life as I was at that moment. Knowing I was close to the ladder, I left the man and went to the bottom of the ladder trying to call for help, but that's very difficult when wearing a Breathing Set, so I climbed the ladder and was hauled out by my comrades. While I had been down in the ship another Petty Officer had got two lads dressed ready to come to my aid, I then cracked up and went completely to pieces feeling bloody useless. After what seemed like eternity with six of us on a rope, we hauled the Petty Officer out where a doctor and myself tried to resuscitate him; at one stage we thought we had got him as he appeared to vomit a thick yellow lumpy substance but after fifteen minutes we knew it was useless and the Medical Officer certified him as dead.

I then wrapped him in a blanket and tied him up having first removed his dog tags and a couple of items that had fallen out of his pocket, whilst we were trying to resuscitate him. Three Medical Assistants from *Hermes* arrived and started to help with our smoke and exhaustion casualties.

Soon after this happened the forecastle deck started to get warm and we had to move to the after end of the ship. In the hanger I found two more casualties who had been efficiently dealt with and another smoke inhalation case, but he was stable, so we went to help on the ammunition train that was unloading 4.5 shells off the stern of the ship. Soon after we started the First Lieutenant appeared on the hanger roof and told us to abandon ship to one of the vessels assisting us. This was when there was the first signs of any panic. Throughout the whole thing it was noticeable that calmness reigned supreme, maybe all that training at Portland and other exercises had paid off in the long run. I went back into the bay and released a back injury from his stretcher and with the assistance of a Chief Petty Officer moved him onboard HMS *Arrow*, and then went aboard myself. He was the last casualty to leave the ship.

To my astonishment I found my casualty with the 66 per cent burns in the hanger awaiting transfer to the *Hermes*, but having said that the Medical Officer and Leading Medical Assistant did all that was possible to save the man's life and probably did it quickly. There was a casualty in the Sick Bay being resuscitated and a couple of shock casualties being treated by first aiders. After sitting, standing and twitching for a while I started to put a full casualty list together with all those missing that could be accounted for, not something that I would want to do again. I went round each mess and warned everybody about chest pains as I was concerned that some people may suffer from blast lungs. Almost everyone on board had to have analgesics for headaches, but luckily we didn't have any cases of blast lungs.

We lost 20 men. Four Chief Petty Officers, four Petty Officers, three Officers and nine Junior Rates, the vast majority being chefs. A total of

28 casualties reported but the accurate figure is just over 40 because a lot of the shock cases recovered as did a lot of the exhaustion and smoke inhalation casualties, therefore they were not recorded.

Going back to the start, the smoke spread throughout the superstructure very quickly and it was a very thick black acrid smoke. To describe it I will tell what happened to our Petty Officer Gunnery Instructor, his action station was at the 20mm machine guns, he was making his way there at a run when he entered the smoke on 01 deck, he found himself on his hands and knees and that was in the open air. What it was like in the ship doesn't take much imagination, there the fumes were as bad if not worse.

When I went back into the Sick Bay the last time it appeared that there had been people in there smoking, you could see straight across it but there was a haze, and I nearly coughed my lungs up. The best way to describe the smell is that of trichlorethylene, only a million times worse. A number of people managed to escape using their respirators, unfortunately some people thought they could go into smoke filled compartments with them on. One paid the highest price of all, his life. Others were more fortunate but only just. The after end remained virtually free but the forward end was bad mainly because of all the doors on the starboard side were buckled and couldn't be closed properly.

The blast: The missile came in under the galley deck and exploded in the engine room, blowing up the galley, Chief's Mess, Wardroom, Petty Officer's dining room and cabins on 02 deck damaging doors on both starboard and port passageways. It lifted the MCO panels off their mountings and blew part of it into HQ1. There was considerable structural damage within the ship, the fire main was blown apart and the CO2 drench couldn't be reached at any time. The helicopters coming to our aid at one time appeared to fan the flames.

The casualties came in various groups, the first were the initial injured from the mess, then the shock cases followed by smoke inhalation finally by exhaustion. Many of the exhausted ones were alright while they were fighting the fires but as soon as they were relieved they collapsed and were useless for a while until they regained their senses. A lot of the initial shock cases recovered very quickly with little treatment.

When we abandoned ship and had time to sit and reflect everybody suffered from some form of shock, some deeper than others. Fear of a strange ship. Fear of being hit. Sadness of losing friends, a ship and all personal belongings. It's an incredible feeling to see nearly everything you own going up in smoke, the only things you've got left are the clothes you stand up in, it is a very strange feeling.'

Selected Bibliography

Becket, Cdr W. T. N. Naval *Customs, Expressions, Traditions* (Gieves 1931)

Coulter, Surg Cdr J. L. S. *The Royal Naval Medical Service* Vols I and II

Dickenson, George. Staff Surgeon RN Manual of Instruction for RN Sick Berth Staff

Hampshire, A. Cecil. *The Royal Navy since 1945* (Wm Kimber, 1975)

Holman, Thomas. *Life in the Royal Navy* (Samson Low, Marston, 1892)

Jarrett, Dudley *British Naval Dress* (Dent and Sons 1960)

Keevil, Lloyd and Cooper *Medicine and the Royal Navy* (Vol IV)

Lewis, Michael *Navy in Transition* (Hodder Stoughton 1965)

Lloyd, Christopher *Nation and the Navy* (Cresset Press 1961)

Plumridge, John *Observation on Diseases in the Army*

Smollet, Tobias *Roderick Random* (Dent)

Revell A. L. *Haslar the Royal Hospital*

Also consulted were the quarterly editions of the *Mariners' Mirror* and *Journals of the Royal Navy Medical Service*

Index

–Strength 1st W. War 32
–Strength 1939 40
–Strength 1943–5 42
–Specialisations 27, 42
Sick Berth Petty Officers'
   Efficiency Medals 115–121
SB Chief and Petty Officers,
   introduction of 36
Sick and Hurt Board 4
'slops' 17
Smollet, Tobias 8
Special Duties officers 47
'square rig' 47
St Vincent, Earl 11
St John Ambulance
   Brigade 30–31
State Registration of Nurses 42
Supplementary List Officers 60
Surgeon's Mate 5, 9

'Tiffy', Sick Berth 22
Tjitjalengka, HMHS 68
Training system in Royal Navy
   '69, introduction of 53
Trotter MD, Thomas 10
typhoid, immunisation
   against 32

Uganda, HMHS 70–71
Uniform, SB early 17
–1891 22

–1956 47
–Surgeons 18
–Wardmaster officers 35, 47

Vasna, HMHS 67
Ville de Paris 11
ventilation in men-of-war 21
Vita, HMHS 69–70
VAD'S, strength in 1945 43

'waister' 6
Wardmaster Commander,
   introduction of 50
Wardmaster officers–
–strengths 16, 27, 40, 42, 52
–increase in tasks 49
–Special Duties List 47
–change in name 53
–uniforms 35–6
Wars – Crimea 14
–South African 27
–Spanish Civil 41
–1st World 30
–2nd World 40
water supply to ships in 19th
   century 20
Warrant Rank, end of 45
'Way ahead' scheme 46

X-Factor in Pay 51
X-Rays 27

Printed in the UK for HMSO
Dd 736275   C32 8/84